SOME VISTAS OF MODERN MATHEMATICS

SOME VISTAS OF MODERN MATHEMATICS

dynamic programming,
invariant imbedding,
and the
mathematical biosciences

by Richard Bellman

UNIVERSITY OF KENTUCKY PRESS

To
DR. LOUIS BERLINROOD
friend and mentor

PREFACE

This age is one of the great ages of mankind.

As such, it is a time of ferment. All over the earth, we witness the birth pangs of new societies and new cultures. In our own country, it is a period of emancipation. Some are escaping from the tyranny of centuries-old prejudice, others from the blight of inherited poverty. All of us are gradually emancipating ourselves from cheerless puritanism and are looking forward to freedom from the dread diseases and disabilities that have plagued humanity from the beginning.

Science by itself plays no major part in shaping the philosophical attitudes that make human beings desire a better world for themselves and others. Once, however, these attitudes have been formed, science plays a fundamental role in making the wishes come true. To grow the food to feed the hungry, to introduce effective birth-control measures, to build cities and to make them habitable, to staff and supply the hospitals, to perform a thousand other tasks in a complex society, we urgently need the scientist's help. Inasmuch as mathematics is the language of science, we can readily conclude that mathematics itself must occupy a major position in the world of the future.

It follows that we must pay careful attention to the kind of mathematical training given in the colleges and universities. This is the reasonable view of a society that needs mathematics for its feasible operation. It is an important view because so much of the financial support of the schools comes from the state and federal government. It is hard to see how we can avoid the conclusion that the taxpayer has a right to know how his tax dollar is spent. In all conscience, we cannot cry "academic freedom" or "research" or some other convenient slogan and claim immunity from a critical gaze.

In addition to being a tool of science, mathematics is also an art form. It possesses its own structures and its own esthetic goals. How well are we turning out young artists? We know from a study of the contemporary scene, or from the histories of the other art forms, that the fields of painting, sculpture, literature, and the drama all react strongly to periods of turmoil in culture and technology. Professional mathematicians, dedicated both to research and to passing on the torch, are very much concerned with the sluggish reaction of the universities to the new developments within mathematics itself, to the new interactions between mathematics and science, and to the significance of the computer. No art form can remain static without becoming sterile. Mathematics is no exception to this universal rule.

Between the formless entity called "society" and the ethereal concept of artistic conscience is something quite real and tangible, the individual. Just as we are not dedicated solely to creating an efficient state, so we are not merely high priests at the sacred shrine of mathematics. We are very much concerned with the happiness of the individual, with his growth, fruition, and emotional satisfaction. We know that his university training, particularly his graduate training, will be a determining factor in his life.

If we take this responsibility seriously, as the overwhelming majority of university professors do, it is essential to discuss openly the many different choices that exist as far as both training and research are concerned. Furthermore, we must attempt to point out the possibilities for success and happiness in these directions. It is imperative to let the student know which fields are promising and which ones have been well worked out for twenty-five years. He may wish to make a deliberate choice to work on the Riemann hypothesis or the four-color problem. But he should be aware of the probabilities of success in these endeavors as compared to a number of other activities.

Much of current university education is woefully wrong because it is narrow and provincial, providing no broad view of the exciting activities of the outside world. It calls to mind the following paragraph from *Gulliver's Travels:*

"There was a Man born blind, who had several Apprentices in his own Condition; Their Employment was to mix Colours for Painters, which their Master taught them to distinguish by feeling and smelling. It was indeed my Misfortune to find them at that Time not very perfect in their Lessons; and the Professor himself happened to be generally mistaken: This Artist is much encouraged and esteemed by the whole Fraternity."

Discussions of matters like this are frustratingly difficult because we cannot pursue them in the same manner in which we present a mathematical proof. We cannot expect to establish any principles in a rigorous fashion. Nor can we pursue the discussion purely rationally. Much is subjective; much is a matter of judgment. But this perhaps is the major point. We must bring this fact clearly to the student's attention so he is forced to exercise his own judgment and common sense rather than accept unquestioningly the traditional material. If we can only get him to ask, "Why?" instead of just "What?" we will have made an essential step in his education. We are not interested so much in determining his precise path as in forcing him to make his own decision from a wide range of worthwhile choices. This procedure is difficult. We must enthusiastically promote certain ideas and theories because we believe they merit study and research, yet we must constantly point out the existence of still other points of view and other endeavors. The task is not easy for a human being. As Mark Twain might have said, it wouldn't be a cinch for an angel.

The purpose of this book, originally delivered as lectures at the University of Kentucky during Thanksgiving week of 1966, is to describe some of the ways that the problems of the modern world provide interesting mathematical questions and open up entirely new domains of mathematics. Rather than concentrating solely on "What," I have indeed tried to answer "Why," even at the risk of some verbosity here and there. In particular, I have constantly emphasized the fact that there are many alternate formulations of physical processes in mathematical terms.

I hope that this book will be of interest to a number of different groups of readers. To the student, I hope it will provide some discussion of why certain mathematical theories are created and where and how certain types of problems arise. To the practicing mathematician in another field and to the scientist, I hope it will satisfy his curiosity as to what is going on in other parts of the forest. To the chairman of a department, or to a dean, I hope it will be useful in planning the new curriculum for the department of mathematics or in explaining the many different kinds of interaction that can exist between a computer installation and the Department of Mathematics. I have tried to preserve some of the informal flavor of a lecture in the presentation.

The expansion and revision of these lectures was carried out with the support of the National Science Foundation under Grant No. GP–6154 and of the National Institutes of Health under Grant No. GM–14633–01, and I wish to record my appreciation to these agencies for their support.

RICHARD BELLMAN
University of Southern California
1967

CONTENTS

one

DYNAMIC PROGRAMMING

AND MODERN CONTROL

THEORY

1. Introduction

Let me state at the outset that this chapter will be resolutely kept on an expository level. As any academic mathematician knows, it is easy to take refuge in complicated equations that present every appearance of profundity. Unfortunately, in addition to boring the reader, this approach would bore me, and my minimum requirement for a lecture is that I be entertained.

Therefore, instead of the usual "Satz-Beweis" display of erudition, it will be more interesting to roam about in the fields of dynamic programming and control theory, pointing out where some of the problems and ways of solving them arise. In so doing, I will discuss a number of ways in which the digital computer is exerting profound and irrevocable influences upon mathematics.

2. Where Do Research Problems Come From?

Some years ago, I read a story by Isaac Asimov, one of my favorite science fiction authors, about the world of fifty or one hundred years hence, when computers have become so complex and powerful that ordinary scientists are not allowed to use them.

To use a computer efficiently requires a rigid competitive training from childhood. People who have taken the appropriate courses and have passed the qualifying tests are called Computer Masters and granted the privilege of playing with these giant toys indefinitely, and in any way they please. Nobody is allowed to interfere with their activities, no matter how strange the experiment they want to conduct or how wasteful it seems. It might be pointed out, parenthetically, that this is somewhat analogous to the situation today in the field of high-energy physics and in the man-in-space program.

The story continues: A certain Computer Master is observed by his distinguished colleagues and worshipful students spending his days and nights reading jokes into the machine. This behavior is considered rather eccentric even for Computer Masters; but because the penalty is severe for disturbing any of this exalted rank in the course of his activities, nothing is done to hinder him.

After three weeks of intensive effort, he ceases his endeavors and returns to his usual haunts, exclaiming, "I have discovered it!" Naturally, his colleagues are curious about what he has discovered. "Well," he says, "the question that kept nagging at me was the classic one, 'Where do jokes come from?' " To utilize all the contemporary resources at his disposal to answer the question, he had read thousands of jokes from many sources into the computer. All its enormous powers were then used to analyze the stories in accordance with various theories and disciplines, ranging from philology to psychology.

Finally, the computer printed out the result of this intensive analysis. Jokes, it concluded, are constantly being fed into our world by a civilization from outer space, which then observes their distribution, variants, and effects. Thus the Earth is being used as a giant laboratory, and all human beings are guinea pigs in this massive psychological experiment. Anyone who has ever tried to make up even a passable joke, much less a good joke, will accept this as a reasonable explanation.

What struck me when first reading Asimov's story was that graduate students, and in all likelihood most college and university teachers, have much the same idea about research problems. Where do research programs arise? I firmly believe that the average graduate student thinks that they somehow come down from the sky like

UFO's, float down the river in a basket, or are found neatly printed out next to the university computer each morning.

One of the major contributions that we can make as teachers is to convince students by example after example that a large fraction of all significant research problems, even in a field as abstract as mathematics, arise in a sensible and natural fashion from the problems of the outside world. Many mathematicians, of course, prefer not to believe this. They would rather believe in some remote divine origin, no matter how obscure, than admit that the problems they work on have a physical reference, or even that there is a rational way of choosing questions to investigate.

I leave as a significant research problem for possibly psychiatrists, and for historians of culture, the task of explaining why some human beings should delight in believing that what they have devoted their life to is completely unrelated to human affairs. Another unresolved question is why presumably educated and cultured persons should scorn anyone who devotes a reasonable part of his intellectual activity to improving human conditions on earth, and indeed pride themselves on their own separation from reality.

3. What Does One Do Next?

Every once in a while, despite careful planning, I am trapped in some sort of faculty–graduate-student tea. Desperate for diversion at these times, I usually entertain myself in tormenting graduate students by asking them questions. One of my favorites is, "Where did you find the problem you are working on?" Most students, incredulous at such an obviously stupid question, answer quickly, "From my professor, of course."

Not so easily diverted, I then ask a second question: "What are you going to do next if you solve this problem?" This is an uncontemplated catastrophe, and even the thought leaves them dumbstruck. The problem is their blanket. As a matter of fact, the calamity of solution is one that many research groups do not think about sufficiently. A true story illustrates this.

About twenty years ago, when mathematicians were grossly underpaid (as opposed to the present time, when they are merely underpaid), one of my friends was delighted to obtain a summer consulting job at an aircraft company on Long Island. The organization was paying as much as $25.00 or $30.00 a day for his services, and he was naturally eager to justify their munificence. Recall that these were the days when assistant professors at major universities were paid $3,000 a year—that is, those with clear evidences of ability and future development.

On the first day after the end of the school term, he went to see the head of the engineering group, who promptly gave him a mathematical problem of some interest to the company. Being conscientious, industrious, and well motivated by the prospects of continuing consultation, he started in on the problem immediately and worked hard at it all through the night at home. An excellent analyst, he was able to carry through the complete solution sometime near daybreak.

He reported the next morning, bleary-eyed but triumphant, and proudly presented his solution. The head of the research group looked at the solution, stared in horror, and then sadly exclaimed, "My God, you've solved our summer problem!"

The point I would like to emphasize in this connection is that successful research depends, not upon the solution of a succession of isolated individual problems, but upon the forging of a connected chain of both problems and solutions. It is essential to have an open-ended program plotted out so that the solution of one problem does not leave one scouting about for something else to do. Each problem should lead naturally to further problems; each solution, to further solutions.

4. The Behavior of Systems

Let me now indicate how the physical world provides an unending series of interesting and formidably difficult problems in the area of control theory. My own interest in this area started with my thesis in 1946 on stability theory. In order to explain what stability theory is, I must begin with some preliminary ideas.

Consider a system, a concept that we will for a moment leave undefined, but whose general nature may be understood intuitively. One basic problem in mathematics and mathematical physics, and, indeed, throughout the physical and social sciences, is first to describe the behavior of a system in a convenient fashion, then to use the description to predict future behavior, and finally to apply this crystal-gazing ability in some useful way.

In mathematical parlance, we have a state vector that is known. On the basis of this information we wish to determine the state vector at some future time. The mathematical device we use to answer this question is very simple, yet ingenious. As a matter of fact, we become so accustomed to using the device that we begin to forget that it is a device. We become blasé, take it entirely for granted, and eventually come to regard it as the only approach. In general, we tend to forget that mathematical and logical approaches to problemsolving are very different from the ordinary workings of the human mind. I shall return to this point.

For example, we may want to predict tomorrow's weather from the weather at noon today. The mathematician attempts to solve this problem in an interesting fashion. He first imbeds the original problem within a family of related problems, and then proceeds to ascertain the weather by first predicting it a minute ahead, then two minutes ahead, and so on until he reaches the twenty-fourth hour.

The person who asked the question may justifiably complain that he doesn't want that much information. After all, most of the time he doesn't really care about the weather at two o'clock in the morning. All he wants to know is whether he can play tennis or golf the next day. The mathematician at this point apologizes profusely for this deluge of numbers, namely the states of the system at all intermediate times; but, he admits that it is the only way he knows to handle the problem. To determine the behavior of a system at a particular time in the future, generally we must be able to determine its behavior at any time in the future. How to avoid this proliferation of data is a fundamental problem whose importance is just being appreciated.

The trick involved in this perfectly legal fortune-telling, of course, is the use of differential equations. If $x(t)$ is the state vector of dimension N, we employ a vector differential equation of the form

$$\frac{dx}{dt} = g(x), \; x(0) = c, \tag{1}$$

to obtain the value of $x(t)$ at all future times. This vector equation corresponds to a system of N simultaneous differential equations.

Proceeding step-by-step by means of standard numerical techniques, we can go from the present state to any desired future state—at least conceptually. This is the essence of classical mathematical physics.

In the majority of cases, the basic equation is a partial differential equation, or a functional equation far more complicated in form, rather than a differential equation of the type just shown. But the principle is the same, although the analytic and computational aspects may become tremendously more complex. As a matter of fact, without the slightest trouble one can keep oneself profitably and happily engaged for life investigating the many different types of functional equations that arise in the physical, engineering, biological, and economic spheres. With the aid of the digital computer, this endeavor is far more feasible and less frustrating than it was even twenty years ago.

5. Approximation and Stability

Some of us, however, with the attention span of bright chimpanzees, become a bit bored working repeatedly on the same type of problem, so we look about restlessly for different kinds of questions to investigate. We don't want to change fields too drastically, because it would involve a painful amount of study and learning of new methods. Nonetheless, we do want some novelty in our pursuit of the reluctant muse of mathematics; consequently, we are willing to undertake a reasonable amount of intellectual retreading from time to time.

Let us do this and investigate the matter of the prediction of the behavior of the system in greater depth. We assumed in Eq. 4.1 that the system was denoted by a finite-dimensional state vector. Everyone in the engineering and scientific worlds knows that a physical system cannot be described in so simple a fashion. For example, it is very well to consider a planet or a spaceship as a point particle in six-dimensional space described by three position coordinates and three velocity coordinates, a six-dimensional phase space. Many important results can even be deduced in this fashion. But neither a planet nor a spaceship is a point particle, as anyone can plainly see.

What I am emphasizing is the fact that every mathematical formulation of a physical process involves a good deal of idealization and approximation. The complexity of any physical process effectively prevents us from starting an investigation in any different fashion. We must agree initially to concentrate on some particular aspects of the system, and to eliminate others from a preliminary mathematical model. We cannot take account of all available physical concepts, phenomena, and measurements from the very beginning.

Furthermore, when we write down a differential equation such as Eq. 4.1, we are assuming a very simple cause and effect relation. Essentially we are saying that the rate of change of the state vector depends only upon its current value. Furthermore, since we have agreed in our preliminary considerations to limit the number of state variables, it is impossible, under this assumption, to write down from first principles an exact equation involving only the selected variables. In any physical situation, the rate of change of the selected variable depends upon others we have left out. The behavior of these omitted variables in turn depends upon still other quantities, and so on, ad infinitum. Consequently, we must employ some combination of mathematical and physical reasoning to obtain what is called "closure," namely a finite set of equations solely in terms of the agreed-upon variables.

Hence, we must face the fact that every equation we employ to describe the physical world is approximate. Furthermore, since it is impossible to measure the initial state to an arbitrary degree of accuracy, we know that the initial values used in the calculation of the solution are slightly incorrect. In addition, we know that any method that we employ to solve the equation in numerical terms will introduce additional errors—errors due to the kind of approximation used to obtain a computational solution and errors due to the fact that a digital computer has a limited arithmetic accuracy, "round-off" error. Analog computers possess different types of limitations.

We see, then, that in applying mathematics to the scientific world, we are constantly in situations where we are taking account neither of all the variables, nor of all the interactions between the variables; where we cannot measure anything precisely; and where we cannot perform accurate calculations even if the equations and input data are precise.

At this point, after the foregoing explanation of what constitutes a mathematical model, a reasonable person may tend to start looking for a different field of endeavor. The public, even the scientific public, is usually quite discouraged when it learns about this state of affairs, because it prefers to believe in magic methods that solve all problems. The latest candidate to accomplish this fact is, of course, "The Computer."

The public is likely to say, "You're destroying my faith in science. Do you mean to say that science is not true, that science is not exact, and that I am left with nothing that I can think of as absolutely, irrevocably true?"

The mathematician can only shake his head sadly and acknowledge that this is the way the world is. This situation reminds me of an anecdote I read recently in *Saturday Review*. A famous philosopher of both science and law, Morris Rafael Cohen of CCNY, was giving a lecture trying to point out the approximations that are fundamental parts of any philosophical attitude. After the lecture, a coed said, "You have destroyed my faith in life. Don't you have anything to replace it?" Morris Rafael Cohen replied, "My dear young lady, you might remember that one of the labors of Hercules was to clean out the Augean stables—he was not required to fill them up again."

Granted that every equation and every measurement is approximate, the question then arises as to what confidence we can have in the predictions of the associated theory. This is a problem in *stability theory*. We must ask ourselves, "Is it true that the answer derived from an approximate formulation is a reasonable approximation to the answers given by more exact formulations?"

Clearly, this question is one of the basic problems of science, and it is equally clear that it can never be answered completely. What we will have over time is a hierarchy of theories of greater and greater sophistication yielding more and more accurate answers to more and more questions. But there will never be an ultimate theory that is "exact." To some people, this fact may be disappointing; to others like myself it is exciting and challenging to see how far we can get.

In any case, we obviously have been doing very well in our explanation of the universe over the past three hundred years, and there is no reason to suspect that we will not do much better over the next three hundred, using these same pragmatic attitudes.

6. Typical Problems of Stability Theory

Leaving aside philosophical aspects, let us consider some basic problems in stability theory. In mathematical physics and engineering, we begin by studying small disturbances from equilibrium and are thus led to linear differential equations:

$$\frac{dx}{dt} = Ax, \quad x(0) = c. \tag{1}$$

Here x is, as before, an N-dimensional vector. This equation can be analyzed completely in simple analytic terms when A is a constant matrix.

To obtain Eq. 1 from an equation such as Eq. 4.1, we assume that second-order terms are negligible and that there are no external disturbances over time. If we take these realistic features into account, we obtain a more general equation of the form

$$\frac{dy}{dt} = Ay + g(y) + h(t), \quad y(0) = c. \tag{2}$$

The major problem confronting us is to estimate for $\|x - y\|$ (where $\| \cdot \|$ signifies an appropriate norm or measure of the magnitude of a vector) in terms of estimates concerning the degree of nonlinearity of $g(y)$ and the magnitude of the external disturbance $h(t)$. This kind of question was first investigated in depth by Poincaré and Lyapunov, who were motivated by many problems in celestial mechanics.

Similar but more complex problems arise when we take account of time lags and hereditary processes. Here the base equation is a differential-difference equation, a simple version of which is

$$\frac{dx}{dt} = Ax(t) + Bx(t - \tau), \tag{3}$$

where τ is a positive constant. When we consider processes described by infinite-dimensional vectors, the initial linear equation may be a partial differential equation such as

$$u_t = u_{xx}. \tag{4}$$

Closure introduces further questions of stability. Suppose, in Eq. 3, that τ is small compared to the t-units employed, and we take advantage of this fact to replace Eq. 3 by the approximate equation

$$\frac{dx}{dt} = Ax(t) + Bx(t) - B\tau\frac{dx}{dt}. \tag{5}$$

What is the relation between the solutions of Eq. 3 and 5?

Similarly, suppose in place of Eq. 4 we have a nonlinear equation such as

$$u_t = u_{xx} + u^2, \tag{6}$$

subject to the conditions $u(x, 0) = g(x)$ where $g(x)$ is periodic of period 2π. To obtain an analytic and computational hold on the solution, we write

$$u = \sum_{n=-\infty}^{\infty} u_n(t)e^{inx}. \tag{7}$$

Substituting in Eq. 6 and equating coefficients of e^{inx}, we readily obtain an infinite system of ordinary differential equations

$$u'_n(t) = -n^2 u_n(t) + g_n(u_0, u_1, u_{-1}, \ldots), \, n = 0, \pm 1, \ldots, \tag{8}$$

where $g_n = \Sigma_k u_k u_{n-k}$. Suppose that we truncate by taking $u_n \equiv 0$ for $|n| > N$ and replace Eq. 8 by the finite-dimensional system

$$u'_n(t) = -n^2 u_n(t) + g_n(u_0, u_1, u_{-1}, \ldots, u_N, u_{-N}, 0, \ldots), \tag{9}$$

$n = 0, \pm 1, \ldots, \pm N$. What relation is there between the solution of Eq. 8 and 9? This question is particularly important today because equations such as Eq. 9 can readily be solved numerically with the aid of a digital computer for values of N of the order of several thousand. This means that we possess a direct systematic approach to the numerical determination of the function $u(x,t)$.

Finally, let us indicate how the very process of the numerical solution itself introduces questions of stability. To solve an equation such as Eq. 2 computationally via a digital computer, we ordinarily employ some type of difference approximation. Say that we replace Eq. 2 by the difference equation

$$\frac{y(t + \Delta) - y(t)}{\Delta} = Ay(t) + g(y(t)) + h(t), \, y(0) = c, \tag{10}$$

where t now assumes only the values $t = 0$, Δ, 2Δ, ... This procedure is not efficient, but it illustrates the ideas. Again the problem arises: For small Δ, is the solution of Eq. 10 close to that of Eq. 2?

We see, then, how various types of natural physical, analytic, and computational approximations lead directly to stability problems. Stability theory is one of the foundations of mathematical physics and engineering. It is basic to many investigations.

7. After Stability Theory, What?

It is clear once again, from the kinds of problems I have sketched in Sec. 6, that one can easily work indefinitely on significant questions in the field of stability theory. I stayed in it long enough to write a Ph.D. thesis and to gather the material for my first book.

Surveying the situation twenty years later, I feel that my decision to leave the field was wise.[1] Many more books and papers could be written, and are being written, and hundreds of formidable problems remain. But the field is difficult; and as far as I can see, no significant new ideas or techniques have been added either in the last twenty years or in the fifty years before—the time between the work of Poincaré and Lyapunov and my thesis.

Consequently, the problem I faced in 1948 was to use in a new area the experience and analytic skill I had acquired in studying stability theory. What should that area be? As usual, a series of incidents and accidents determined the course of events. Let me, however, present an excellent *ex post facto* argument.

The solution to the problem can be obtained by means of simple psychological analysis of classical science. Basically, the classical scientists were observers, because they were forced to be observers. The focus of classical science was celestial mechanics. When one studies the solar system and attempts to explain and predict its idiosyncrasies, it is apparent that neither human theory nor human observation is going to have any effect on the actual motion of the moon, the rising of Venus, or the occurrence of the next eclipse.

Consequently, it is natural to think solely in terms of descriptive theories of the universe. In any case, the question of the stability of the solar system is of some interest, particularly for long-term plan-

---

[1] Not for the logical reasons that follow, but because I wanted to work in analytic number theory. How I got from there to control theory is another tale.

ners. Indeed, it is pertinent to note that this fundamental problem has never been resolved. For all we know, the next Gemini shot may be the crucial one that starts the final countdown.

8. Control Theory

Coming closer to contemporary times, as man began to understand more of the fundamental forces of nature, we note a change in the scientist from the role of the observer to that of the doer.[2] "Doing," of course, has always been the fundamental objective of science. We understand so that we can do something with that understanding. When we can do nothing with our understanding, we try to console ourselves with thoughts of *ars gratia artis,* "knowledge for knowledge's sake," and other picturesque phrases. But it should be clearly understood that this is a type of intellectual sour grapes.

I do not deny the pleasure of puzzle-solving and the satisfaction of human curiosity, nor do I denigrate the esthetic aspects of abstract mathematics. Edna St. Vincent Millay's phrase, "Euclid alone has looked upon Beauty bare," is a bit extreme, but it contains a great deal of truth. Yet all this is only part of the picture. The grown, mature man wants more than puzzle-solving, more than intellectual voyeurism, and more than esthetics. He wants to be an activist. In the familiar words of the Bible, "There is a time for all things." There is an austere beauty to functionalism as well as to abstraction.

Mankind's history has been a struggle against a hostile environment. We finally have reached a point where we can begin to dominate our environment and cease being victims of the vagaries of nature in the form of fire, flood, famine, and pestilence. We are at a time when we wish to cease wagering our existence upon the outcome of a race among the Four Horsemen of the Apocalypse. As soon as we understand this fact, our mathematical interests necessarily shift in many areas from descriptive analysis to control theory. There is, of course, no clear line of demarcation. Fortunately, this ill-defined situation is exactly what we want because it permits

---

[2] Consider, however, that the title of high priest of Rome was *pontifex maximus,* i.e., "chief bridge-builder."

us to proceed into new areas a bit at a time without unduly straining our brain cells or suffering from intellectual culture shock.

An additional fact is also clear. More sophisticated and powerful mathematics is necessary if we really wish to be doers rather than observers. Indeed, the history of mathematics shows clearly that the growth of vital mathematics depends crucially on continuing inter- action with the real world. Thus, new engineering, economic, and medical objectives will result inevitably in new mathematical theo- ries that we can safely predict will illuminate the dusty shelves of the past where many classical problems repose.

9. Control Processes

Suppose that a system is not behaving in a totally desirable fashion. What can we do about it? We encounter this kind of problem in engineering, in economic and industrial systems, and in the biomedical domain.

The system under observation may be unstable under slight per- turbations, which is undesirable in an uncertain world; or, although the system is stable, its return to equilibrium is too sluggish for our tastes. Or it may be that we want to impel it to a totally different mode of behavior, which may require a good deal of effort if the original "orbit" is highly stable.

We must find ways to formulate problems of this nature in precise mathematical terms. Then we must decide whether or not the problems once formulated justify an intense effort. Not all problems are equally significant at all times.

10. Maxwell and Vishnegradsky

There are many ways to formulate control problems in mathe- matical terms. The earliest work, initiated by Maxwell and Vishne- gradsky, was in what would now be considered the area of *design* rather than *control,* as we shall see in a moment.

It is interesting to note parenthetically that the net result of an excellent contribution by Maxwell, one of the great scientists of the nineteenth century, was to point control theory in a less than opti- mal path for about seventy or eighty years. It is salutary to keep in mind that first-rate people can have very bad, sometimes disastrous, effects on a field. I shall illustrate this phenomenon by showing briefly how classical control theory went wrong. Many further examples could be given, possibly in a future series devoted to this fascinating area of cultural history.

Let us review Maxwell's approach. He was searching for a mathematical theory that would explain the governor[3] used by Watt for his steam engine and a number of other control devices as well that were developed in the course of the Industrial Revolution in England in the mid-nineteenth century.

One aspect of control is to maintain a system either in a desired state or in a desired mode of behavior. Let us here consider the simpler of the two problems, maintenance of equilibrium. To see what this means in analytic terms, we proceed along the following lines. Suppose that the system is described by a state vector x, an N-dimensional vector, and that the dynamical equation is

$$\frac{dx}{dt} = g(x), \tag{1}$$

with $x = 0$ as the desired equilibrium state, i.e. $g(0) = 0$.

If $x = 0$ is not a stable solution, we require some additional force to maintain the system in equilibrium. The idea behind that of Watt's governor, and that of the other governors, was *feedback control*. The system is designed ingeniously so that any deviation from equilibrium automatically generates a correcting force that tends to restore the system to equilibrium. In the simplest case, this restoring force is directly proportional to the disturbing force. Although this case may appear to be simplest mathematically, from the engineering point of view, an "on-off," or "bang-bang" control is more desirable.

This idea of feedback sounds good in theory, but how do we know that the new system is really any more stable than the old? Consider, for example, the task of riding a bicycle, a good example of a highly unstable system in the upright position. For a person to ride a bicycle, continuous feedback control on his part is required.

When we first attempt to ride, the correcting force exerted is usually far too great, with the result that subsequent corrections

---

[3] The Greek version of the word "governor" is the origin of the contemporary term "cybernetics."

induce greater deviations that introduce more drastic corrections and still greater deviations, and so on, until disaster occurs. Consequently, it is not at all obvious that proportional control is always what is desired. Indeed, it might well be that feedback control maladroitly applied can accentuate the original disturbance. This phenomenon is part of the problem faced in attempting to avoid either a depression or inflation in a national economy. Actions of federal control boards to raise or lower interest rates, or a president's decision either to economize or pump-prime, if out of phase, can easily accelerate a trend in the wrong direction.

The point I want to emphasize is that control of complex systems is basically difficult, which means that a great deal of careful analysis is required before theories are to be taken seriously in making decisions in the real world. On the other hand, doing nothing is a definite control action that is often costly. I hope that I have succeeded in alerting you to the fact that the control of actual systems is difficult.

11. Small Perturbations

Maxwell rightly felt that a mathematical analysis of this basic question of stability under feedback control was in order, and he proceeded in the following fashion. Let

$$\frac{dx}{dt} = Ax + g(x), \; x(0) = c, \tag{1}$$

be the equation of the system with feedback control effects included. Assume for the moment that only small deviations from the equilibrium position will occur, and let $x = 0$ denote this state. Suppose further that $g(x)$ represents second-order and higher terms in the components of x.

If the initial disturbance c is a vector of small magnitude, it is plausible that it is sufficient to study the linear equation

$$\frac{dy}{dt} = Ay, \tag{2}$$

in order to determine the stability of the control system. Subsequently, this assumption was examined in great detail by Poincaré and Lyapunov (who were, as mentioned, primarily concerned with celestial mechanics) and was shown to be sound in a number of important cases. There remain, however, many complex aspects of this general question concerning the validity of the use of approximate equations to determine properties of the solution of the original equation.

The interesting point about using Eq. 2 as a discriminator is that the stability of its solution can be determined in a purely algebraic fashion by examining the location of the characteristic roots of the coefficient matrix A. If all the real parts of the characteristic roots are negative, all the solutions of linear equations approach zero as $t \to \infty$; thus small initial disturbances damp out.

Inasmuch as these properties of A depend on the actual numerical values of its elements, we see that by means of a suitable choice of the components of the system, we can ensure stability, which is what I meant when I said that this type of investigation is more suitably dubbed "design" than "control." However, I cannot emphasize enough that there is no clear-cut line of demarcation between the two activities. Too often, these activities of design and control are considered distinct, with the result that a complex system is designed by people who bear no responsibility for its actual operation and control.

12. Enter the Laplace Transform

At this point, a number of people realized that the Laplace transform could be used to study linear differential equations with constant coefficients.[4] Using this technique, the solution of Eq. 11.2 can be expressed in terms of the matrix

$$F(s) = (A - sI)^{-1}, \tag{1}$$

where s is now a complex variable, using a contour integral. Furthermore, the effect on the location of the characteristic roots of changes in the elements of A, i.e. of changes in design, can be followed in an elegant fashion in the complex plane.

This step was certainly very useful. However, it was then followed by the drastic step of omitting all mention of the behavior of the system in the time domain and thereafter concentrating solely

---

[4] Cauchy first pointed it out.

upon transfer functions, phase diagrams, and so on in the s-plane. Consequently, until quite recently if one glanced through a book purporting to discuss control theory, he found very pretty discussions of loops and curlicues in the complex plane but very little about the dynamics of the original system. What started out as control theory became a series of ingenious applications of the theory of functions of a complex variable. The very concept of feedback control disappeared from the engineering literature!

One difficulty, of course, with this metamorphosis is that a student trained in this school has a great deal of trouble readjusting his sights to the real world of engineering. If one introduces him to realistic factors of contemporary systems such as constraints and nonlinearity and, what is more, stochastic and adaptive effects, he has a certain tendency to shrug his shoulders fatalistically and say, "I don't understand how to handle these effects in control processes. Therefore, I will ignore them." Back to diagrams!

13. Psychology and Research

To understand the history of human culture, even of mathematics and physics, it is essential to understand human psychology. Abstract logic and the textbooks imply that it is customary and ordinary, when faced by a new problem that cannot be treated by the methods currently employed, to discard the old, ineffective methods and to develop some new ones. However, human logic dictates—and human history confirms—that instead we throw away the problem and pretend that it does not exist. Furthermore, those people who point out the weaknesses of the old theories and the need for new ones are usually mocked, scorned, and regarded as troublemakers or, at very least, as people who refuse to join the team effort. If, however, they are fortunate enough to live long enough, they survive the transition, break the thought barrier, and become "pioneers in human thought." Finally, they become members of the scientific establishment, duly orthodox, and as opposed to change as the old guard they replaced.

I could go into this characteristic behavior in greater detail both in control theory and in many other fields in and out of science, but I think that there is not much need. One can trace, from Maxwell on, a number of distinguished people who industriously helped control theory go wrong. The skeptical reader interested in the details may consult any standard text on "control theory" of about five years ago.[5]

14. Mathematical Formulation of Control Theory

Let us, then, reexamine the problem of control and see whether we can introduce a more meaningful formulation that will allow greater flexibility of action. In so doing, the probability is high that we will introduce some new and significant mathematical problems. Furthermore, in the back of our minds is the comforting knowledge that we now have available a tool for the feasible solution of these problems which was not available to Maxwell, nor even to people of twenty years ago—the digital computer. With this instrument at our disposal, we don't have to be smarter to do much better than our predecessors. Newton's remark can be paraphrased to read, "on the consoles of computers."

To avoid any complications initially, let us consider that a system is described by a single scalar function, $u(t)$. In the absence of any control action, the equation for the system would be

$$\frac{du}{dt} = g(u), \ u(0) = c. \tag{1}$$

Let us suppose that the control action is represented by the function $v(t)$, the control variable, and that the result of this action is to change the original equation into the equation

$$\frac{du}{dt} = g(u, v), \ u(0) = c. \tag{2}$$

The problem we face is to choose the function $v(t)$ in an efficient fashion.

One way to approach this basic problem is to appreciate the fact that in every control process, there are at least two objectives. First of all, we want to improve the performance of the system or equivalently to decrease the cost of the deviation of the system from desired behavior. Second, we must take account of the fact that it

---

[5] This was written in the enlightened days of 1967.

costs something to exert control.[6] Consequently, we have to balance these two types of costs, consistent with the general principle of "nothing for nothing" in this world.

We have, then, two costs, one measured in terms of the state of the system, $u(t)$, and one measured in terms of the control variable $v(t)$. To measure these costs precisely, let $w(t)$ be the desired time behavior of the system, and let

$$\int_0^T h(u - w)dt = \text{the cost of deviation from desired performance} \quad (3)$$
over the time interval $[0, T]$,

where h is a specified function, e.g. $h(u - w) = |u - w|$. Further, let

$$\int_0^T k(v)dt = \text{the cost of exerting control over the time} \quad (4)$$
interval $[0, T]$,

where again k is a given function. Taking these costs to be in the same units (which is often and perplexingly not the case), it is reasonable to add the two costs and obtain the total cost,

$$J(u, v) = \int_0^T [h(u - w) + k(v)]dt. \quad (5)$$

It is now equally reasonable to pose the following optimization problem: Minimize the functional $J(u,v)$ over all functions $v(t)$, where the functions u and v are connected by the differential equation, Eq. 2.

If we consider more general systems described by a state vector $x(t)$, we are led pursuant to the preceding considerations to the following problem: Minimize the scalar functional

---

[6] This concept is very difficult for accounting offices of large organizations to understand. There is a constant battle with bursars, comptrollers, vice-presidents, and so on to persuade them to accept the obvious fact that it is not worthwhile to employ an accounting procedure that requires fifty dollars worth of time, effort, and resources to keep track of a fifty-cent item. Unfortunately, university administrative offices, in general, maintain the prewar attitude that the time of professors is free and therefore can be ignored in bookkeeping. In particular, paperwork by the faculty costs nothing—to the accountant. From discussions with visitors from many parts of the world, I am prepared to state that this problem is not only national, but universal and transcends cultural, political, and ideological differences.

$$J(x, y) = \int_0^T g(x, y)dt, \qquad (6)$$

over all vectors y, with x and y connected by the differential equation

$$\frac{dx}{dt} = h(x, y), \ x(0) = c, \qquad (7)$$

and y is subject to the condition that $J(x,y)$ be well defined.

The cognoscenti will observe that this is a problem in the calculus of variations, a classical mathematical theory.

15. Control Theory and the Calculus of Variations

This fact has been very helpful in the scientific rejuvenation of a number of experts in the calculus of variations. It is certainly not a bad idea; indeed, as a result of this renaissance of a classical theory many interesting and important problems are now being attacked under the spur of control theory. Obviously, the many varied types of physical systems, the conglomeration of costs, and the different types of control that exist present a delightful potpourri of optimization problems. Furthermore, an excellent side effect has been the widespread dissemination throughout the scientific world of a number of powerful variational techniques that until quite recently were buried in obscure and difficult papers and in Ph.D. theses of the University of Chicago school. Glancing through a number of texts in mathematical physics and control theory of about 1957, one received the distinct impression that the calculus of variations stopped with the work of Euler and Lagrange—or, at least, that the authors' knowledge did.

If, however, the sole purpose of modern control theory was to rejuvenate and renovate professionals in the calculus of variations, one could not feel that any major contribution had been made. It would have been a worthy activity, but not startlingly significant.

The important point is that the major aims of control theory are different from those of the calculus of variations, which had its source in mathematical physics. As mentioned, mathematical physics is basically a descriptive theory, whereas control theory is a domain for activists. The objectives of control theory are thus distinct from those of the calculus of variations in its classical cloak. Naturally, the infusion of the new ideas of control theory will have a decisive effect upon the future course of the calculus of variations, just as the techniques of the calculus of variations will strongly influence the growth of control theory. But control theory is a new and genuinely different theory for reasons I will discuss later. It follows that the way to generate interesting new mathematics is not to examine a control process, say, "Ah, that is a problem in the calculus of variations," and then dismiss it. We have to keep clearly in mind the aims and purposes of control theory, a mathematical theory strongly intertwined with the systems of the real world. It is thus very much broader in scope.

16. Numerical Solution

A strong objection to the classical calculus of variations as portrayed in the textbooks is that there is never any mention of the sizable difficulties encountered in attempting to obtain a numerical solution. Indeed, in the beginning, I felt that I was very dense whenever I found myself incapable of carrying through a detailed numerical solution, because this aspect of the variational problem was not discussed in the texts. Therefore, one might draw the normal conclusion that the task must be beneath discussion. Actually, of course, the situation is just the reverse.

In applying a mathematical theory to an actual control process, we must first establish the existence of a numerical algorithm. It is absolutely essential that we possess a feasible means of providing a numerical answer to a numerical question.

As we shall see, the severe difficulties associated with solving optimization problems along classical lines have motivated new analytic formulations of control processes, using dynamic programming and other techniques. Again—an important point—the desire to obtain numerical results can even force us to a new analytic formulation of a physical process. The ability to carry out large-scale arithmetic calculations with the aid of the digital computer reinforces the search for new methods. I shall return to this theme in chapter 2.

17. Steady-state Control

Another aspect of control processes that is foreign to the calculus of variations is the emphasis on long-term behavior of the system. Transient behavior is, of course, crucial in many instances; but in many other types of processes, steady-state behavior is basic—what we might call "asymptotic control theory." As I shall emphasize later, the study of approximate behavior in general becomes crucial.

18. Constraints

The presence of constraints both on the allowed behavior of the system and on the types of control that can be imposed is another important feature of realistic control processes. In an idealized mathematical problem, we can speak in general and convenient terms. When considering a specific physical process, we must have at our disposal techniques powerful and flexible enough to take account of local idiosyncrasies of the particular system.

For example, if we are trying to determine an optimal trajectory, from point P to point Q, we want to rule out trajectories that look like Figure 1. Nor do we want a path that looks like Figure 2.

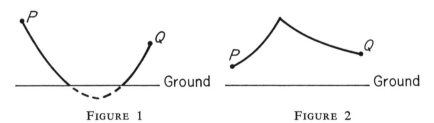

FIGURE 1   FIGURE 2

There are obvious objections to the first trajectory. We object to the second path for a different reason. A rapid change of direction of this kind can produce a blackout in the pilot or serious damage to the plane.

These simple examples show that realistic control processes come ready-made with various constraints on the type of path that can be followed, or the type of control that can be exerted. Consequently, a never-ending source of new kinds of control processes is furnished by the outside world with its engineering, economic, and biomedical processes.

19. It Takes Time to Exert Control

From about 1937 to 1967 some powerful techniques have been developed for solving variational problems subject to constraints. These include the techniques of the calculus of variations polished from 1937 on by Valentine, Graves, and Hestenes, the "maximum principle" of Pontryagin, and others, and the newer gradient techniques, search methods, nonlinear programming algorithms, methods of quasilinearization, and successive approximations, and so on. Expositions of these methods will be found in the references at the end of this chapter. Much remains to be done in these areas before we can feel confident of our mastery of them. Nevertheless, let us go on to even more interesting aspects of control processes. In order to formulate some important mathematical problems connected with realistic control processes, it is necessary to analyze carefully what controlling a system means. Here we are following the historical pattern set by both quantum mechanics and relativity theory; that is, a detailed analysis of the *operational* aspects of a physical system leads to new scientific problems and eventually to new theories.

What, then, does exerting control mean in practice? Let us examine the operation of determining the state of the system at time t. This operation involves using sensing devices to observe the system, then processing the measurements obtained. This processed data is fed into the control device, which transmits signals that result in the desired control being exercised. A basic problem is to extract information from the mass of data. Information is required for decision-making (Figure 3).

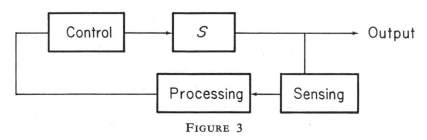

FIGURE 3

It is clear that all these operations require *time*. Hence, a control process necessarily introduces time lags, which means that a mathematical formulation of a control process involves far more than

ordinary differential equations. It involves differential equations
with time lags, equations usually called differential-difference equations. Ordinarily, when we write a differential equation of the form

$$\frac{dx}{dt} = g(x, y), \ x(0) = c,$$
(1)

we assume tacitly that y depends upon the state of the system at
time t. When, however, we take into account the time lags due to
gathering, processing, and utilizing data, we see that it is more
reasonable to suppose that y depends upon the state of the system at
some time in the past, say $t - \Delta$. Thus, in a very natural fashion, the
study of control processes enlarges the kinds of functional equations
that are of interest. Furthermore, a little thought shows that the
amount of time required to control the system depends upon the
state of the system itself. Thus, we are led to study equations where
the time lag depends both upon the state of the system and the
nature of the control actions. Under various assumptions concerning the nature of the control process, we are led to equations of the
form

$$\frac{dx}{dt} = g\{x(t), x[t - \tau(x, t)]\}.$$
(2)

Equations of this type also play an important role in respiratory
control processes, and in many fields of physics such as electrody-
namics.

20. Macroscopic Principles of Uncertainty

Let me turn to some of the problems connected with the control
of large systems. As I have pointed out, if we observe only a few of
the state variables and employ a simple control law, we use up a
small amount of time. If, however, we insist on observing all the
state variables and use a complex law, we consume a larger amount
of time. It follows that when we have a large system to control, we
have a choice between using a small amount of data and making an
early choice, or taking a long time to observe a great deal of what is
going on before deciding. The decision is difficult. Either we make
some errors in control because we do not have all the available
information, or we consume a lot of time making a decision, during

which time the system has been going its own way without suitable guidance.

An analysis of this situation leads us to conclude that, analogous to the microscopic principle of uncertainty of quantum mechanics, there is a macroscopic principle of uncertainty in control theory. *There is no way to control a large system perfectly.* This is tied up with the fact that two basic costs are involved, the cost of obtaining data, and the cost of the time required to process and employ this data.

21. Large Systems

The conclusion to which we are slowly wending our way is that a new genre of mathematical problem has arisen in the last few years—controlling large systems. Furthermore, it is not even a question of control; that is much too ambitious. It is a question of feasible operation.[7] Those of us living in big cities, afflicted by air pollution, water pollution, traffic jams, noise, overcrowding, and all the other "blessings" of big city civilization, can appreciate this point.

There is little difficulty nowadays in using any of several methods to obtain either an analytic or computational solution of the determination of optimal control of a system specified by two state variables. As computers become more powerful and as our analytic tools are sharpened, we can begin to feel confident of obtaining detailed solutions when faced with four, or eight, or sixteen state variables.

But if one examines some of the problems connected with the control of the American economy or, on a much more humble level, with the feasible operation of a chemical refinery, he begins to realize how far we are from understanding problems of this nature. The conventional descriptions require thousands upon thousands of equations, subject to the demands of "on-line" control.

The general problem of operating a large system with a limited amount of time available for observation, data processing, and implementation of control, generates new kinds of mathematical

---

[7] See the article in the February 1967 issue of *Fortune* on the problems of the U.S. Post Office.

questions that have not yet been precisely formulated, and certainly not resolved.

22. Distributed Variables

I shall mention briefly some other aspects of reality that lead to new types of mathematical problems. If we consider the control of systems involving heat flow, we encounter partial differential equations rather than ordinary differential equations. As soon as we begin to enter the domain of science to any extent and consider the many different processes ruled by partial differential equations, we meet new types of analytic problems and ever more formidable computational problems.

23. Tacit Assumptions

The problems I have mentioned so briefly generate more than enough potential research to occupy the lifetimes of many people. Nevertheless, it is just the beginning, a quick peek into the future. To obtain a better idea of the new domains that have been opened up, we must go back to the foundations, to the basic conceptual and analytic formulations, and to analyze in careful detail the control processes we have been talking about.

There are many assumptions between the lines of a formulation of the control of a system based on differential equations. We assume that the state of the system can be described as a finite-dimensional vector and that the state can be observed instantaneously and with complete accuracy. Cause and effect are taken to hold and, moreover, to be known. Finally, we suppose that we know the objective of the control process.

The principal difficulty of dealing with control processes in the real world is that none of these assumptions are verified. In general, we do not know how to describe the system in terms of a finite-dimensional state vector. Even knowing this vector, we do not possess an accurate understanding of cause and effect. Nor do we know how to evaluate the performance of the system, and we usually do not know the length of time over which to make this evaluation. Moreover, dismaying as it is, we have other obstacles with which to contend.

In many cases, the costs of control and the reward for good performance are in different units. We cannot simply add these quantities or manipulate them in a direct arithmetic fashion, since the units are incommensurable. It is one thing to use a quantitative formulation when there is a common unit such as dollars or time that we can use to produce a scalar utility, but what do we do in studying the problem of automation when we have to compare output of goods with the dangers of social dislocation? I shall merely mention this bugaboo of incommensurability and return to the simpler problems of the preceding paragraph.

If we want to study the problem of rational decisionmaking in realistic situations involving complexities of the kind mentioned above, we must somehow deal with uncertainty. One of the first facts that emerge as questions of the foregoing nature are studied is that the classical treatment of uncertainty, the mathematical theory of probability, is helpful, but only in a very rudimentary fashion. The real problems of control in the face of unknown effects escape these simple confines.

A first step is to analyze different kinds of uncertainty. Here the mathematician becomes uncomfortable inasmuch as he finds himself forced to think about profound philosophical questions such as: What do you mean by rationality in the face of ignorance? How does one measure rational decisionmaking when there is uncertainty concerning cause and effect?

There will never be precise answers to questions of this nature. There will be classes of answers, with the responsibility clearly upon the decisionmaker for the kind of theory he wishes to employ. In the following section I will show how theories of this nature can be constructed.

24. Feedback Control

One way to see what to do when random effects can arise in the course of a control process is to return to a deterministic control process and to note what choices we actually have as to the determination of optimal control. Consider, for example, the problem of minimizing the functional

$$J(u) = \int_0^T g(u, u')dt, \tag{1}$$

over all functions for which $J(u)$ is defined and for which $u(0) = c$.

To answer this question, one belonging to the calculus of variations, we can employ a natural extension of the procedure used in calculus to handle finite-dimensional minimization. We regard the minimizing function $u(t)$ as a point in function space and vary about it in order to obtain a variational equation, the Euler equation.

This equation in this case is

$$\frac{\partial g}{\partial u} - \frac{d}{dt}\left(\frac{\partial g}{\partial u'}\right) = 0, \tag{2}$$

with the additional boundary condition $\partial g/\partial u' = 0$ at $t = T$. It is generally nonlinear, which combined with the two-point boundary condition, makes for both difficult analysis and numerical solution (Figure 4).

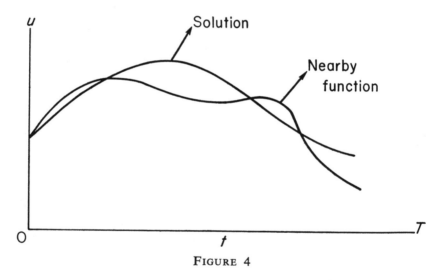

FIGURE 4

Similarly, when we have a more complex problem, that of minimizing the functional

$$J(u, v) = \int_0^T g(u, v)dt, \tag{3}$$

where u and v are connected by the differential equation

$$\frac{du}{dt} = h(u, v), u(0) = c, \tag{4}$$

we can regard $v(t)$ as a point in function space and vary about it to obtain another differential equation, which together with Eq. 2 specifies the class of candidates for the minimizing function.

This procedure is not to be lightly dismissed when deterministic processes occupy our attention; indeed, it is very powerful and versatile, but what do we do when there are chance effects? What do we mean by "optimal"?

To set the stage for the use of control techniques of a different nature, let us reexamine the idea of feedback control. I mentioned before that feedback control went bad with the aid of mathematicians. But a scientific idea of this power and versatility should have sufficient vitality to survive this traumatic experience.

What is the basic idea behind feedback control? Feedback control, as exemplified by the Watt governor and many other devices of this nature, implies the following: "Observe the state of the system at any time and see whether you like its behavior. If it is not behaving properly, exert an influence to modify its behavior. The type of control action that you employ should depend on the type of observed deviation from desired behavior."

Note that this type of control is very different from that of the calculus of variations, which prescribes the time behavior of the control variable. Feedback control asks that the control variable be a function of the state of the system.

As an aside, let me point out that anyone familiar with computers knows that there are two distinct and very important ways to use computers. The first is based upon instructions that tell what the computer is to do at a specified time. The second is based upon instructions that tell the computer what to do when a certain event occurs. We become so accustomed to the luxury of thinking in terms of time, that very convenient scalar variable, that we occasionally forget that there are entirely different ways of keeping track of what is going on.

Frequently, it is not necessary to ask about the time at which a certain event occurs in order to produce the desired behavior. Whenever a car hits a bump in the road which affects its direction, we turn the steering wheel; whenever the speed of the car exceeds a certain limit, we use the brake; and so on. The basic injunction of feedback control is, "Don't be time-oriented; be event-oriented."

Obviously, this way of handling control processes, and decision-making in general, is more flexible than that based on the calculus of variations. Furthermore, this technique handles uncertainties as easily as it treats deterministic processes, and it allows for learning, as we shall see.

25. On Coney-chasing

To illustrate in simple terms what I mean by event-orientation rather than time-orientation, consider the classic problem of a dog chasing a rabbit, a well-known problem in elementary differential equations (Figure 5). We suppose that the rabbit is constrained to

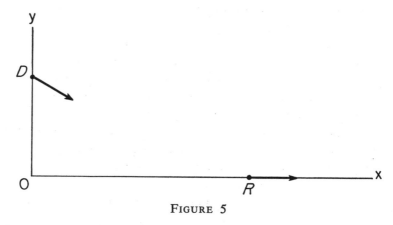

FIGURE 5

travel along the x-axis and that the dog chases the rabbit, pointing toward it at all times. Let the speed of the dog be v_D and that of the rabbit be v_R, with $v_D > v_R$.

Given the initial positions, the distances OD and OR, and the quantities v_D and v_R, we wish to determine the time at which the dog will overtake the rabbit. When a problem of this type is given to a graduate student in mathematics, the calculus syndrome visibly takes over. His right hand begins to twitch in an uncontrollable urge to cover the page with differential equations.

Given the slightest encouragement, he can make the numerical solution to this problem unbearably complex. The interesting point in this case, and in so many similar situations, is that we can easily

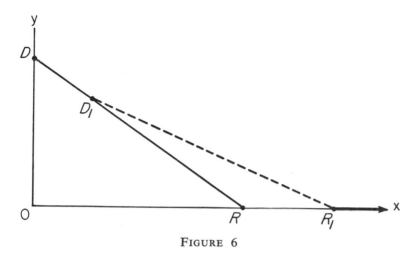

FIGURE 6

teach a twelve-year-old to solve this problem numerically to a reasonable degree of accuracy with nothing more than a rule in about five minutes. Given a digital computer we can do arbitrarily well, using only elementary algebra and geometry.

We only have to simulate the process. We begin by connecting the points D and R and measure along this line the distance that the dog will travel in one time unit, which determines the new position D_1 (Figure 6). The point R_1 represents the position of the rabbit at the end of one time unit. We repeat the process with the points D_1 and R_1. When the dog is within one time unit of catching the rabbit, there will be an overshoot. Consequently, we can easily estimate the order of error of this procedure and choose our time units so that an acceptable answer is obtained.

Nothing in this numerical algorithm could not be taught in high school. I wish to emphasize by this example the simplicity and naturalness of analytical and computational procedures based on event orientation. From the standpoint of dynamic programming, we are employing the concept of "policy." The control action that is taken depends on the state of the system.

26. Stochastic Pursuit Process

One of the amusing aspects of the difference between the classical approach and the approach I have just described is that the twelve-year-old has no difficulty adapting this procedure to the problem of catching a rabbit who swerves unpredictably, or who falls down once in a while, nor of finding out what happens if the dog is nearsighted. The Ph.D. in mathematics who attempts these questions along conventional lines encounters formidable analytic and conceptual difficulties.

Carrying out a control process in terms of following a policy is thus ideally made for dealing with chance effects. In the face of uncertainty, we agree to modify our behavior according to the actual run of events. What could be more natural?

27. Dynamic Programming

I have been leading up to a formulation of control processes, and of multistage decisionmaking in general, in terms of the theory of dynamic programming. Fortunately, the multistage decision processes to which I was first exposed were of stochastic type.[8] Consequently, regardless of my early training in classical analysis, I was forced to think in terms of policies. Indeed, only after many years of dealing with stochastic decision processes and equally many years trying to handle deterministic control processes subject to constraints along classical lines, did it occur to me that if we could handle uncertainty in the manner suggested, then we could equally well handle deterministic processes using the new mathematical techniques.

It would be nice to pretend that I carefully analyzed what was involved in both deterministic and stochastic control processes from the very beginning, then followed a logical approach that led to the general method of dynamic programming, but this was not the case. It took an embarrassingly long time before I realized how easy it was to formulate deterministic control processes in terms of policies, or even before I contemplated this possibility. We all wear such intellectual blinders that it is amazing that anything new is ever developed.

28. Functional Equations

I shall briefly indicate how a straightforward generalization of the ideas behind the method used in the dog-rabbit pursuit problem

[8] At the RAND Corporation in 1948.

leads to a new approach to the calculus of variations and to the study of interesting new kinds of functional equations.

Consider once again the problem of minimizing the functional

$$J(u) = \int_0^T g(u, u')dt \tag{1}$$

over all functions satisfying the initial condition $u(0) = c$. We now regard the determination of the minimizing function, the optimal trajectory, as that of finding a direction to follow at each point P in the (t, u)-plane. It is clear that either this type of direction or the conventional representation $u = u(t)$ enables us to draw the curve in Figure 7. This direction is thus to be a function of the state of the

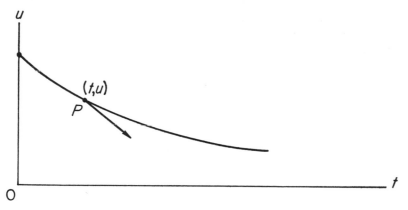

FIGURE 7

system. In this case, the two state variables are c, the current position, and either t, the current time, or T, the time remaining. Since the process is homogeneous, we can employ T here conveniently.

Let us denote the minimum of $J(u)$ as a function of the initial values of these variables,

$$\min_u J(u) = f(c, T), \tag{2}$$

and proceed to obtain an equation for $f(c, T)$[9] (Figure 8).

Let v denote the value of $u'(0)$. Then v is itself a function of c and T, which we write as $v(c, T)$. Let Δ be a small quantity and

[9] The idea behind this approach will be discussed in detail in chapter 2.

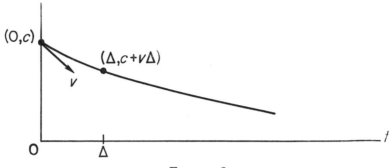

suppose that v is a continuous, and even differentiable, function of c and T. We can make very strong assumptions at this point because we are interested only in exhibiting the formalism. Then a choice of v over the interval $[0, \Delta]$ is equivalent, to terms in Δ, to a choice of $v(c, T)$. This function that determines the direction to take, i.e. the decision to make, is called the *policy function*. As a result of the initial choice of v, we see that the following changes occur in the state variables,

$$c \rightarrow c + v\Delta,$$
$$T \rightarrow T - \Delta.$$
(3)

Furthermore, since the functional is additive,

$$J = \int_0^\Delta + \int_\Delta^T ,$$
(4)

we see that once arrived at the state $(c + v\Delta, T - \Delta)$, we proceed from this new position in time and space to minimize a functional of exactly the same type as before, namely the integral $\int_\Delta^T g\,(u, u')\,dt$. This is an instance of the Principle of Optimality, the basic principle of the theory of dynamic programming. Hence,

$$f(c, T) = \int_0^\Delta g(u, u')dt + f(c + v\,\Delta, T - \Delta) + 0(\Delta^2)$$
(5)
$$= g(c, v)\,\Delta + f(c + v\,\Delta, T - \Delta) + 0(\Delta^2),$$

for some policy function $v(c, T)$. We use the simple estimate $\int_0^\Delta g\,(u, u')\,dt = g(c, v)\Delta + 0(\Delta^2)$. In order to determine the function $f(c, T)$ optimally, we minimize the right-hand side over v, obtaining the relation

$$f(c, T) = \min_{v} [g(c, v) \Delta + f(c + v\Delta, T - \Delta)] + 0(\Delta^2). \qquad (6)$$

Continuing our formal analysis, let us write $f(c + v\Delta, T - \Delta) = f(c, T) + \Delta v(\partial f/\partial c) - \Delta(\partial f/\partial T) + 0(\Delta^2)$ and cancel the common term $f(c, T)$ on both sides. Dividing through by Δ and taking the limit as $\Delta \to 0$, we obtain the nonlinear partial differential equation

$$\frac{\partial f}{\partial T} = \min_{v} \left[g(c, v) + v\frac{\partial f}{\partial c} \right], f(c, 0) = 0. \qquad (7)$$

This nonlinear partial differential equation determines both functions, $f(c, T)$ and $v(c, T)$. The reader can amuse himself by counting the number of steps that require justification. The number is about the same as the number of unjustified steps in the usual derivation of the Euler equation.

29. Discussion

From this equation we can derive all the standard results of the calculus of variations, ranging from the Euler equation and Hamilton-Jacobi theory to the Pontryagin maximum principle. One advantage of the foregoing approach is that it takes account of constraints on v in a very simple fashion. If the choice of v is constrained by a condition such as $|v| \leq h(c)$ or $v = \pm 1$, or generally $v \epsilon R$, where R is a region of v-space dependent on c and T, we replace Eq. 28.7 by

$$\frac{\partial f}{\partial T} = \min_{v \epsilon R} \left[g(c, v) + v\frac{\partial f}{\partial c} \right], f(c, 0) = 0. \qquad (1)$$

Another fundamental point is that this equation is of initial-value type as contrasted to the two-point boundary equation of classical variational theory. This fact allows us to employ computers in a reasonably direct fashion when the dimension of the state vector is not too large. The definition of "large" is here time dependent. As of 1967, five or ten may seem large. Within ten years, we will be able to think comfortably of ten or twenty.

In the classical calculus of variations, the Euler equation is first derived formally, then justified by a detailed analysis. Similarly, in the theory of dynamic programming, it is necessary to examine carefully the conditions under which Eq. 1 holds. Depending on the constraints, $\partial f / \partial c$ can have discontinuities. The situation is similar to what prevails in the equations of gas dynamics where shocks can occur.

30. Duality

I have described in the preceding pages two different approaches to control theory leading to different analytic formulations. What is the relation between these two methods? We suspect that two approaches that yield equivalent equations must be connected in some fashion. The answer is very interesting. The calculus of variations and dynamic programming correspond to the dual approaches to Euclidean geometry.

As we know, we can base Euclidean geometry on two undefined objects, points and lines, that satisfy certain incidence relations. If these relations are written carefully, it is easily seen that the roles of the two undefined objects, points and lines, can be interchanged without affecting the abstract formulation. This means that when proving geometric theorems we have a choice of using either the point-line form or the line-point form, whichever is more convenient or more intuitive to us.

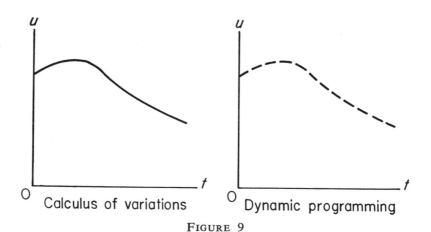

FIGURE 9

Thus, we can consider a curve to be a locus of points or an envelope of tangents. The calculus of variations corresponds to a curve being taken as a locus of points; dynamic programming views a curve as an envelope of tangents (Figure 9).

As might be expected, this duality is very important from both the analytic and computational points of view. Several very powerful numerical algorithms now available rely on a continued interaction between the original and a dual problem.

This duality, however, exists only for deterministic processes. As soon as we turn to the study of stochastic and adaptive control processes, we find that the calculus of variations and dynamic programming represent very different modes of behavior.

31. Operational Considerations and Stochastic Processes

I have mentioned the fact that mathematical and scientific advances come about when a physical process is analyzed in fine detail and, in particular, when every aspect of its operational feasibility is examined. To illustrate this fact, let us take the dynamic-programming approach which is event-oriented and ask ourselves about what is involved in carrying out a control process according to these principles.

Let us be careful not to make any tacit assumptions, but to see clearly what this formulation entails as far as actual data processing and implementation of control is concerned.

I have said that we observe the system at each time and on this basis choose the appropriate control. Consider what the calculus of variations prescribes. It chooses a function of time, the optimal control function, then never bothers to observe the system from the initial state on. According to this approach, once we have decided what to do, we do not look at the system again.

How can we interpret these concepts when we accept the existence of uncertainty? One way to interpret the phrase "never bothers to" is to say that we are not able to. Hence, we can say that in the face of uncertainty, the classical approach is invoked in situations where it is impossible to obtain any further information concerning the process, and dynamic programming is used when we do possess means of observing the system in operation and of utilizing the data obtained in this way. In other words, we use dynamic programming when we possess complete or partial information concerning the state of the system at each time, but we use the classical approach when we must make an *a priori* decision and subsequently have no chance to correct it as further information is obtained.

This difference is a very exciting thought to the mathematician. It means that when we introduce uncertainty in decisionmaking, we automatically introduce a spectrum of processes intermediate between the "locus of points" formulation and that of the "envelope of tangents."

In order to analyze mathematically these new kinds of control processes, we must introduce the basic concept of "information."[10] What was completely neglected in a classical theory of control was the examination of the kinds and accuracy of the information available to the decisionmaker. Today we have all possibilities before us. At any given time, we can assume that no information is available, that all information is available, or that various kinds of partial information is ascertainable. Furthermore, we can introduce the idea of interrupted control processes where there are probabilities of certain kinds of data being unavailable at any time. The many categories of possible kinds of uncertainties have not yet been systematically explored.

Once we have attained this plateau of sophistication, we can introduce the possibility of a choice of the kind of information we want for decisionmaking at any time. Let us further realistically accept the condition that either we have only a specific time for decisionmaking, or we have a specific number of sensing devices with various capabilities. The problem then arises of deciding what parts of the system to observe, what kinds of accuracy are required, and when to observe.

Consequently, we can start with the simple idea of a control process and by constant analysis of what is possible, what is available, what constraints exist, and so forth, obtain many new and interesting kinds of mathematical problems. Very few such problems have so far been either formulated or analyzed.

[10] When we use the word "information," we are not referring to the highly specialized theory of coding developed by Shannon and others that has usurped this valuable term. We are thinking in broader and more meaningful senses.

32. Learning

To illustrate this point further, let us consider the phenomenon of *learning*. As soon as we begin to analyze the concept of information, the question of learning arises naturally. If we are given the task of controlling a system about which not everything is known initially, we can try to improve our performance over time by testing and experimenting with different kinds of control actions. We call a process where both control and learning are involved "adaptive."

How does one efficiently learn about a partially known system? This simple question introduces many more new classes of control problems and makes numerous contacts with theories of experimentation, planning, research, and so forth. Once in this fascinating area, we are forced to grapple with the field of artificial intelligence. How does one use a computer to learn effectively?

First, we must define precisely what we mean by "intelligence" and "learning." Clearly there are many different types of intelligence and learning. How do we compare human intelligence with computer intelligence, and generally what analogies and differences exist between human and computer decisions and learning? To begin to answer these puzzling and deceptively simple questions, we need some knowledge of psychology and physiology. Indeed, many people feel that the shortest paths to really effective computers are through the field of neurophysiology.

Such questions, which are much more than we can answer, indicate the new horizons made apparent by the investigation of control processes. It is difficult now to contemplate how these horizons will expand or what control theory will be twenty years from now. But we can be certain that it will be lively.

33. Functional Equations

Before discussing these matters further, I want to discuss the many new kinds of functional equations that arise from dynamic programming.

Let us begin with a general version of a control process. Let p be a point in a space S specifying the state of a system and q be a point in decision space D. If the decision equivalent to q is made when in state p, the system is transformed into state

$$p' = T(p, q), \tag{1}$$

and a return $g(p, q)$ is received. Employing the Principle of Optimality, we see that the problem of obtaining the maximum[11] total return for an unbounded process leads to the functional equation

$$f(p) = \max_{q} \{g(p, q) + f[T(p, q)]\}. \tag{2}$$

If we suppose that decisions are made continuously in time, we encounter equations of the form

$$\frac{\partial f}{\partial t} = \max_{q} \{g(p, q) + [\operatorname{grad} f, T(p, q)]\}, \tag{3}$$

where $\operatorname{grad} f$ is the vector with components $\partial f/\partial p_1, \ldots, \partial f/\partial p_N$, with $p_1, p_2, \ldots, p_N$ the components of p. If p is infinite-dimensional, we must employ functional derivatives to write the corresponding equation. If stochastic effects enter, Eq. 2 is replaced by equations such as

$$f(p) = \max_{q} \left(\int \{g(p, q) + f[T(p, q)]\}\, dG(p, q) \right). \tag{4}$$

This kind of equation arises when we want to maximize the expected value of the total return and assume that we can observe the state of the system before each decision is made. If adaptive processes are considered, p is in general infinite-dimensional, often a probability distribution. In all three cases, the same simple conceptual structure provides a basis for an analytic formulation.

An interesting fact evident from the foregoing is that equations such as Eq. 2, 3, and 4 are the natural extensions of the linear equations of classical analysis. Thus, dynamic programming provides a natural generalization of semigroup theory, and multistage decision processes generate natural successors to the linear equations of classical descriptive theory.

To study the structure of the solutions of the foregoing equations, we can employ various kinds of successive approximations. We can

---

[11] In an optimistic mood, we maximize total returns; in a pessimistic mood, we minimize total costs. The mathematical problems are the same.

approximate to the solution of the functional equation $f(p)$, or we can approximate to the optimal policy function $q(p)$. The important point is that an equation such as Eq. 1 involves two functions, $f(p)$, the return function, and $q(p)$, the optimal policy function. The fact that we can use either to determine the other is an extension of the duality concept already mentioned. Sometimes it is more convenient to work in function space; sometimes the new method of *approximation in policy space* is more efficacious. Often we use both at the same time.

In general, when we approximate in policy space, we obtain monotonicity of approximation to the solution in a painless fashion. This fact, and others, tempts us to try to write other kinds of nonlinear equations in a form like Eq. 1. This idea leads to the theory of *quasilinearization,* which has important computational applications.

34. Approximations and Computers

Let us briefly explore some of the impact of the foregoing discussion on the classical theory of approximation. We can expect it to be considerable, inasmuch as one way to view a computational solution is as an on-line control process designed to ensure maximum accuracy in the final result. To write an effective computer program, we must know the kind of device being used to obtain numbers and the kinds of accuracy and storage facilities available. It is interesting to take a still larger view that the process of numerical solution is a control process in which we are allowed the use of specific kinds of algorithms in a limited time to obtain as accurate an answer as possible.

In particular, we see that it becomes important to think in terms of formulations of physical processes specifically suited to the kinds of computer facilities available. Here we are taking the systems approach, that problemsolving must be viewed as a whole starting from problem formulation through analysis to numerical solution.

For this and other reasons the computer has revitalized several classical areas. Consider, for example, the theory of algorithms. There is significance to the statement that a certain theorem is not decidable in a finite number of logical operations, as there is to the theorem that $\sqrt{2}$ is irrational. In the case of the determination of the

$\sqrt{2}$, we continue and ask for the best rational approximations of a certain type. Similarly in a decision process, either in control theory or in logic, we are more interested in the approximations obtained under certain finiteness constraints than we are in the exact answers. We want to know the best results that can be obtained in a limited time with the aid of specified types of auxiliary algorithms.

Likewise in analysis we realize that a hierarchy of problems is connected with solving an equation. First of all, we must examine the question of existence and uniqueness of the solution. Next, we wish to exhibit a constructive method for obtaining the solution. Then we examine the rate of convergence and its feasibility for various kinds of computers. Finally, we ask for most efficient algorithms subject to the constraints that only certain types of algorithms are available.

35. Computers and Mathematics

It is pleasant to point out that the computer has had a salutary effect in a number of subsidiary intellectual fields where formerly it was quite safe, indeed almost obligatory, to expound general theories embracing wide classes of phenomena. Armchair speculation was safe because the complexity of the processes under study was such that theories could not be proved or disproved. At that stage of human calculating ability, it was impossible to carry out the required arithmetic.

In fields such as economics, cybernetics, artificial intelligence, psychology, and so forth, all sorts of extravagant claims have been made by people with the unfortunate combination of modest education in mathematics and a minimum of scientific responsibility. Indeed, a certain amount of this activity still continues. Gradually, however, the operational point of view is forcing the claim-jumpers out of these fields or at least is keeping them quiet. To introduce a change of subject, ask for the computer program that validates their claims.

If someone asserts that human learning takes some specific form, we can simulate this process on the computer. If the computer program does not achieve its objective, the claim must be withdrawn. Again, if someone insists that he understands how we distinguish between the symbols 2 and 3 on a page, we can test this claim by computer. Gradually it becomes commonplace that understanding must involve operational algorithms. No algorithms, no understanding.

The computer has already greatly affected mathematics, and its effect will increase extraordinarily as its use penetrates the various echelons of academe. However, this device must be regarded in its proper role as an essential part, but still only a part, of the apparatus of the working mathematician.

People who should know better still tend to extreme attitudes when the computer is mentioned. No doubt this reaction is a fear mechanism in operation.

The point must be emphasized that the existence of the computer simultaneously broadens the domain of the mathematician and enhances his role. But I cannot emphasize enough that using a computer properly requires more mathematics, not less. The most difficult part of analysis—that requiring the greatest combination of knowledge, sophistication, experience, and ingenuity—centers about numerical solution. Unfortunately, many mathematicians produced by several distinguished schools—the faithful disciples at a distance of the Bourbaki—have a peculiar, supercilious attitude toward numerical solution of functional equations.

It is amusing, with a wry twist, to see this resurgence of the classical Greek attitude toward science, an abhorrence of experimentation and engineering, an attitude that retarded the development of science for hundreds of years. Galileo introduced the modern intellectual attitude; the Bourbaki caused an unfortunate regression into medievalism. By the standards of this group and its cohorts, Newton and Gauss would not be suitable for membership in the American Mathematical Society.

To sum up, the operational point of view of mathematical analysis, that of providing numerical answers to numerical questions, is the classical one. If I seem to be a rebel by modern standards, it is only because I am a rugged traditionalist.

36. The Mathematical Middleman

The implications of the classical view of mathematics, as aided by the modern computer, are exciting for the undergraduate student. What has been the role of the mathematician in the past? He has been a middleman between the scientist and scientific problems, with a monopoly on equation solving.

Until recently, the mathematicians were the John D. Rockefellers of the scientific world. As you may recall, John D. did not waste his time prospecting for oil. He concentrated on controlling the oil refineries, fully aware that the output of every oil well has to pass through a refinery. This method is a much simpler and safer way to make money from oil than prospecting.

The mathematician was essentially in the same position before the digital computer. The standard route to analysis of a scientific problem was, first, formulation in terms of functional equations, then, analysis of the equation in mathematical terms. Hopefully, this mathematical analysis contributed to the scientific analysis.

The difficulty in following this route is that realistic formulations of physical processes led to formidable functional equations. Because of the mathematician's inability to handle the realistic descriptions, two effects occurred. First, many problems were ignored because they were too difficult; processes involving nonlinear effects, stochastic interaction, and adaptive control, to cite a few, were neglected. Second, the problems considered were first substantially modified to fit the mathematics available; a veritable scientific Procrustean fit. Even today, one finds a continuing emphasis upon linear equations, Gaussian distributions, low dimensional systems, and other convenient idealizations.

This situation is excusable when nothing else can be done. Good mathematics, like politics, is the art of the possible. Unfortunately, people quickly forget the origins of a mathematical formulation with the result that it soon acquires a life of its own. Its genealogy then protects it from scrutiny. Because the digital computer has so greatly increased our ability to do arithmetic, it is now imperative that we reexamine all the classical mathematical models of mathematical physics from the standpoints of both physical significance and feasibility of numerical solution. It may well turn out that more realistic descriptions are easier to handle conceptually and computationally with the aid of the computer, which will have a strong effect on the design of experiments.

Much of the mathematical analysis that was developed over the eighteenth and nineteenth centuries originated in attempts to circumvent arithmetic. With our ability to do large-scale arithmetic, which means the ability to solve thousands (and soon millions) of simultaneous nonlinear differential equations subject to initial conditions, we can employ simple, direct methods requiring much less old-fashioned mathematical training. This ability means that we have more time to present newer, more powerful, and more elegant methods, which in turn implies that across the scientific board the scientist is at last in a position to test theories and hypotheses without a roundabout route through the mathematician.

This situation by no means implies that the mathematician has been dispossessed in mathematical physics. It does signify that he is urgently needed in several classical areas such as statistical mechanics and control theory, and in many new fields, to transform the original mathematical problems to the stage where a computer can be utilized profitably by someone with a suitable scientific training and a basic mathematical training. Essentially, the mathematician's major task is to understand the mathematical formulation well enough to simplify it to the point where he is superfluous.

Unfortunately, this ability of the computer to dispossess old theories and old techniques in favor of new, more powerful, and simpler procedures has produced an academic backlash. The proponents of the classical procedures, resolute blocks to the use of new approaches, are the respected figures in each field, the senior professors, the deans, the people in policymaking positions in the universities and the government. The revolution in arithmetical capability often sweeps away their life's work. An approximation technique of great subtlety that took ten years to develop can be replaced by an exact calculation requiring one minute. How do we get these people to accept these changes gracefully and to introduce the new formulations into the university curriculum? Perhaps the answer lies in the comment of Born that new theories are never accepted; their opponents die off.

Actually, this risk of scientific obsolescence has always been part of the scientific game. There has always been the clear and present danger that a new theory will completely supplant an old one. However, the culture shock introduced in all scientific fields simultaneously by the fantastic amplification factor of the computer makes it difficult to absorb these new ideas and to adapt to them. Essentially, we are viewing an anthropological-sociological revolution as profound as any suffered by a Pacific island culture when first exposed to Western civilization. Seeing how ill-prepared the academic community is for this forcible entry into the twentieth century should make us all a little more sympathetic to the plight of the average citizen in today's bewildering world.

In any case, we face the fundamental educational task of conveying the fact that the basic difficulty in science is to obtain a sensible formulation of a physical process. Once a meaningful formulation has been obtained, we are in an excellent position to apply many simple, powerful techniques for obtaining numerical solutions.

For example, we introduce undergraduate students to the methods of description of physical systems in terms of large systems of differential equations, then teach them to use a computer to obtain numerical solutions. Thus, with a basic education in science, mathematics, and computers, the student can begin to study significant scientific problems while an undergraduate. By the time he enters graduate school or goes into industry, he is ready to study new problems and to carry out meaningful research.

References and Comments

§5. Accounts of modern stability theory will be found in:
> Bellman, R. 1954. *Stability Theory of Differential Equations.* Mc-Graw-Hill Book Company, New York.
> Cesari, L. 1963. *Asymptotic Behavior and Stability Problems in Ordinary Differential Equations.* Academic Press, Inc., New York.

§6. For a discussion of equations involving time lags, see:
> Bellman, R., and K. L. Cooke. 1963. *Differential-difference Equations.* Academic Press, Inc., New York.

For a treatment of the stability of solutions of partial differential equations of parabolic type, see:
> Bellman, R. 1948. On the existence and boundedness of solutions of nonlinear partial differential equations of parabolic types. *Trans. Amer. Math. Soc.,* 64: 21–44.
> Mlak, S. 1957. Differential inequalities of parabolic type. *Ann. Polon. Math.,* 3: 349–54.
> Narasimham, R. 1954. On the asymptotic stability of solutions of parabolic differential equations. *J. Rat. Mech. Anal.,* 3: 303–13.

§8. For a collection of reprints of original papers and discussions illustrating the contents of this and the following sections, see:
> Bellman, R., and R. Kalaba. 1964. *Trends in Modern Control Theory.* Dover Publications, New York.

§9. For more detailed discussion and many additional references, see:
Bellman, R. 1961. *Adaptive Control Processes: A Guided Tour.* Princeton University Press, Princeton, New Jersey.

§10. Maxwell's original paper is reprinted in the Bellman and Kalaba collection noted under §8. See also the September 1964 issue of *Scientific American,* devoted to control theory.

§14. My associates and I pursued the formulation of a mathematical theory of control processes along the lines indicated here from 1952 on at The RAND Corporation. An account of this work, together with references to original papers, may be found in the monograph:
Bellman, R., I. Glicksberg, and O. Gross. 1958. *Some Aspects of the Mathematical Theory of Control Processes.* The RAND Corporation, R–313, Santa Monica, Calif.
The Russian translation appeared in 1962.
Independently, this theory was pursued in Russia by L. Pontryagin and his associates, Mischenko, Gamkrelidze, Boltyanskii, and others. Their work is described in:
Pontryagin, L. S., and others. 1962. *The Mathematical Theory of Optimal Processes.* John Wiley & Sons, New York.
A common stimulus was the "bang-bang" control problem of Bushaw and LaSalle. See:
LaSalle, J. P. 1959. Time Optimal Control Systems. *Proc. Nat. Acad. Sci.,* 45: 573–77,
for a description of recent results. Equally important as far as Bellman, Glicksberg, and Gross were concerned were a number of control processes arising in mathematical economics. See, for example:
Bellman, R. 1954. Bottleneck problems, functional equations, and dynamic programming. *Econometrica,* 22 (No. 4): 517.
———. 1957. *Dynamic Programming.* Princeton University Press, Princeton, New Jersey. Chaps. 8, 9.
———. 1958. Dynamic programming and its applications to the variational problems in mathematical economics. *Calculus of Variations and Its Applications.* Proceedings of the Eighth Symposium in Applied Mathematics of the American Mathematical Society. Lawrence M. Graves, ed. McGraw-Hill Book Company, New York.

§15. For applications of the methods of the calculus of variations, see the book by Pontryagin and others cited under §14 and:
Berkovitz, L. 1961. Variational methods in problems of control and programming. *J. Math. Anal. and Appl.,* 3: 145–69.
Hestenes, M. 1966. *Calculus of Variations and Optimal Control Theory.* J. Wiley & Sons, New York.

§16. For some new types of numerical solution, see:
Bellman, R., and R. Kalaba. 1965. *Quasilinearization and Nonlinear*

Boundary Value Problems. American Elsevier Publishing Company, New York.

§19. The first systematic treatment of differential-difference equations with variable lags is given in the book:
Myskis, L. 1955. *Lineare Differentialgleichungen mit nachteilendem Argument.* Berlin.

§22. See:
Butkovskii, A. G. 1968. *Optimal Control Theory for Distributed Parameter Systems.* American Elsevier Publishing Company, New York.

§27. For a detailed discussion of dynamic programming, see:
Bellman, R. 1957. *Dynamic Programming.* Princeton University Press, Princeton, New Jersey.
————. 1961. *Adaptive Control Processes: A Guided Tour.* Princeton University Press, Princeton, New Jersey.
Bellman, R., and S. Dreyfus. 1962. *Applied Dynamic Programming.* Princeton University Press, Princeton, New Jersey.

§29. For a derivation of these results, see the book:
Dreyfus, S. 1965. *Dynamic Programming and the Calculus of Variations.* Academic Press, Inc., New York.

§31. For further discussion of stochastic control processes, see the book by Dreyfus cited under §29, those cited under §27, and:
Murphy, R. E. 1965. *Adaptive Processes in Economic Systems.* Academic Press Inc., New York.
Stratonovich, R. 1968. *Conditional Markov Processes.* American Elsevier Publishing Company, New York.
See also:
Bellman, R. Some new categories of stochastic processes (to appear).

§32. Processes involving learning are often called "adaptive" these days. For detailed discussion, see Bellman (1961) cited under §27 and the book:
Fel'dbaum, A. A. 1965. *Optimal Control Systems.* Academic Press, Inc., New York.
Further exploration of these ideas of "intelligence" will be found in:
Bellman, R. 1967. Mathematical models of the mind. *Math. Biosci.,* 1: 287–304.
————. 1968. Adaptive processes and intelligent machines. *Proc. Fifth Berkeley Symposium.* Berkeley, California.

§33. A statement of the Principle of Optimality is:
Principle of Optimality. An optimal policy has the property that whatever the initial state and initial decision are, the remaining decisions must constitute an optimal policy with regard to the state resulting from the first decision.

It is deliberately phrased in vague terms so as to maximize its flexibility. In each particular application, its use must be rigorously justified.

§34. For a description of the application of dynamic programming to obtaining numerical solutions, see the book by Bellman and Dreyfus (1962) cited under §27.

two

INVARIANT IMBEDDING

AND MATHEMATICAL

PHYSICS

1. Games Mathematicians Play

Inasmuch as we ended the last chapter on a philosophical note, it is only appropriate to start this one in the same vein.[1] We begin with the hypothesis that a mathematician is basically an irresponsible person. You may smile at this hypothesis; but if you think about it for a moment, comparing the occupation of the mathematician with that of most other inhabitants of other parts of the university or members of other professions, even of the oldest profession, you see that, generally, they perform definite obligations and tasks. The faculty of the medical or engineering school or people in physics and chemistry have reasonably clearly delineated fields of endeavor. But it is not clear, even to himself, what the mathematician's responsibilities are, nor even what constitutes good research. Perhaps in this respect he is closest to the artist, who also encounters serious difficulties when he tries to define precisely what he means by "art."

In any case, in one way, we could define a mathematician as "a

---

[1] This statement is in the same logical category as the story about Sam Goldwyn, the motion picture mogul, who stopped a screenwriter one afternoon at about 3:00 P.M. and asked him why he was leaving so early. "Because," said the screenwriter, "I came so late."

person given a license by society to play games for the rest of his life." And by many standards, playing games is irresponsibility. However, this does not mean that being a mathematician is not a serious pursuit. Personally, I have a British attitude toward games in the sense that as far as I am concerned nothing is more important in life than games. To describe an activity as a "game," then, in no way indicates a lack of intensity when one is engaged in its pursuit. Even irresponsibility has to be taken seriously. Otherwise, the whole effort is wasted and little joy is gained. The point, of course, is that a mathematician can play many different games. And, as in the outside world, one can gauge a man fairly accurately by the kinds of games he enjoys. This point was emphasized by Leibniz.

I continually delight in playing the following game. With a set of theorems that seem reasonably complicated and require difficult and mostly nonintuitive procedures, try to find an approach that will obtain and present the results in a much simpler and more intuitive fashion. In the mathematical world this kind of presentation is usually called "elegant." Probably the most satisfying compliment a mathematician can receive is to have his work called elegant; it is the accolade.

To carry this game one step further, the ultimate object is to make the understanding of some important area of mathematics so simple that future students reading the results will say, "of course." Certainly, one has this attitude upon perusing the research papers of Henri Poincaré, the great French mathematician. As one reads through his papers—written in the beautiful, lucid style that won him election to the French academy as one of the immortals in literature—the uppermost impression is always one of great ease and naturalness. Only when attempting to recreate the results or to tackle analogous unsolved problems, does one realize the mathematical power and careful organization that went into these papers. Comparing these masterpieces of simple, clear exposition with the ponderous German style so typical of the six-hundred-page "Einfuhrung" or with the constipated, crabbed style of the Bourbaki, one appreciates the vast difference between intellectual elegance and the dense academic jargon so popular today. An interesting relic of medievalism is this idea that only the difficult can be distinguished, that only the arcane can be erudite, that what is readily understood cannot be profound.

To return to the game that I like to play: Can we make a powerful mathematical tool simple enough so that a scientist can use it freely?

This goal is a blow at medievalism, in which knowledge is power and the object is to impress, not to inform. Recall that Newton informed Leibniz of his newfound ability to integrate differential equations using power series by means of an anagram. Remarkably, this practice has continued to the present in many scientific journals and books.

The objective cited is in no way intended as an insult to the scientist. I do not ask that a mathematical tool be made simple enough for him to understand. I say that it should be made so simple that he does not have to waste valuable time either attempting to understand it or developing specialized skills in order to use it.

There is a great difference between the modern attitude of maximizing the flow of information and expanding the use of intellectual tools, and the classical concept of hoarding theories in accordance with the precept that knowledge is power. We are back at a point I emphasized in chapter 1, the elimination of the mathematical middleman in the scientific world. Some people may consider my attitude peculiar. Should not a prudent mathematician skillfully obscure and obfuscate so that his talents and skill are essential? I feel that there are more than enough areas that we do not understand and that desperately require the mathematician's attention. He need not worry about technological unemployment, provided that he remain employable.

2. Understanding the Real World

It is relatively easy for the scientist to explain his responsibility to himself and to society. His function is to obtain an understanding of the phenomena of the real world. One of the scientist's principal tools in this endeavor is the mathematical model. Using various mathematical tools, ranging from calculus to group theory, verbal problems are translated into mathematical language.

The hope then is that purely mathematical manipulations will lead to formulas that can be interpreted in physical terms. This idea has been fantastically successful—as a matter of fact, successful beyond anyone's expectations or ability to explain its success. However, if the scientist has to spend inordinate amounts of time learning to manipulate complicated mathematical tools, he is not spending his time doing what he should be doing. On the other hand, if he has to compromise and lower his scientific sights because he has a meager mathematical training, he is unlikely to gain real understanding. Truly, he must walk a narrow path.

The introduction of mathematical techniques, therefore, is a mixed blessing. Without that magic ability called scientific intuition, there is no way to tread a careful route between the Scylla of mathematical complication and the Charybdis of fruitless oversimplification.

This is a brief sketch of the background for the game I wish to discuss. The aim is to take intrinsically complex mathematical theories such as ordinary and partial differential equations, the calculus of variations, combinatorial topology, and so forth, and so arrange the introduction of the concepts and the presentation of the methods that the basic ideas can be easily absorbed by the people who want to use these powerful techniques to solve their scientific problems. Here I shall concentrate on various classes of ordinary and partial differential equations.

3. The Role of the Computer

The game did not get very far until a few years ago for a simple reason: If I were asked for a dominant theme in mathematical analysis over the last two hundred and fifty years, particularly the analysis connected with mathematical physics and engineering, I would say that it is the series of brilliant attempts to circumvent, avoid, and overcome arithmetic. Inability to obtain numbers was the ultimate barrier to understanding in many areas.[2] The principal difficulty encountered in applying the beautiful and basically simple ideas of Newton, Euler, Cauchy, Laplace, Lagrange, and many others was the inability to do arithmetic.

The situation is drastically different now. With the aid of a digital computer, it is relatively simple to verify the amazing accuracy of Newtonian mechanics. Our ability today to obtain the numerical

---

[2] I hasten to note that there are still many areas where we have not reached this barrier because of a lack of comprehension of fundamental principles.

solution of hundreds of simultaneous ordinary differential equations enables us to predict routinely the behavior of planets and their moons on the basis of the inverse square law of gravitational attraction. We can almost equally routinely discover new planets, moons, or comets on the basis of perturbations in the motion of the known ones, or by using other kinds of observations.

Problems that a century or two ago required the combined mathematical genius of Gauss, Laplace, Lagrange, Jacobi, and others for their elucidation, plus truly heroic efforts of numerical calculation by these men[3] and by numerous astronomers, can now be explained in an undergraduate class by an instructor and assigned as homework—provided that a digital computer is available. This phenomenon represents intellectual progress. We can focus on scientific essentials instead of mathematical *tours-de-force*.

The question arises as to whether we can do the same thing in other fields. Can we simplify various powerful mathematical tools to the point where the working physicist, chemist, biologist, or engineer can use them as a matter of course? This question is intriguing.

4. Steinmetz and Electric Circuits

My attention was first attracted to this question by something I read about Steinmetz. Although he can be described as an electrical engineer or a physicist, probably "genius" is a better and simpler term.

The story occurred in a different era, a period when the people in the United States were far more secure than they are now. I mention this fact because Steinmetz happened to be an extreme political radical. He was an anarchist, which is about one stage worse than being a Communist. Furthermore, he smoked cigars relentlessly, which, as far as General Electric, his employer, was concerned, was one stage worse than being an anarchist. The company had an inviolable rule that no smoking was allowed inside the plant. Consequently, because they wanted Steinmetz, they did the only thing they could do, namely build a separate laboratory and "reservation" for Steinmetz where he could wander around billowing smoke to his heart's content.

Steinmetz made many major contributions to the development of

---

[3] Euler went blind in the course of doing calculations of this nature.

the modern American scientific-industrial complex. Perhaps his major contribution was the elimination of Maxwell's equations in the treatment of the most elementary electrical circuits. It is hard to realize that at one time, in order to determine the steady-state current in an RLC-circuit, it was necessary to start with these celebrated equations. Steinmetz realized that the complete mathematical apparatus was not necessary if only the steady-state current was desired in a reasonable frequency range.

All that was needed was the simple formula

$$E = IZ, \tag{1}$$

where Z, the impedance, could be calculated using only elementary arithmetic, given the frequency and the values of the resistor, inductor, and capacitor.

Once this step was taken, it was easy to teach hundreds of thousands of people with only a public school education in arithmetic how to do vital calculations involving electric circuits. It was an essential step in the Industrial Revolution. The day of the electrician had dawned.

5. What About the Computer Revolution?

With the foregoing history in mind, we naturally ask whether we can do something analogous involving the use of the computer. On the premise that we possess a tool for doing arithmetic a million times faster than ever before, and soon a billion times faster and a billion-billion times faster, as I shall indicate later, it seems plausible that we can tackle mathematical physics in ways which are quite different than those of classical vintage which now grace the accepted texts. Is it not reasonable to suppose that all the classical formulations of physical processes, many dating from the eighteenth and nineteenth centuries, should be carefully examined for their operational validity in the twentieth century?

Should we not accept the fact that most of these formulations were guided by the contemporary ability to do arithmetic and to carry out experimentation? After all, the scientists of two hundred and one hundred years ago were just as intelligent, just as imaginative and just as bound by common sense as we are. Consequently, no one a hundred or two hundred years ago would consider that a formulation of a problem was reasonable if it involved the numerical solution of one hundred simultaneous nonlinear differential equations. He might think initially in these terms, but he would immediately try to find different kinds of approximate approaches that would be more amenable to the capabilities of numerical calculation of the day.

This is the principal reason that one sees so little of nonlinear equations in classical analysis. The physicists and engineers of the past were not unaware of the fact that the world is resolutely nonlinear. This absence merely indicates their resignation to the fact that there is little point in writing down nonlinear formulations of theories if there is little chance of getting numbers out of these equations. Even philosophy ultimately rests upon pragmatism. After all, before the computer it was painful enough to get numbers out of linear equations. Even today, with the digital computer available, the experienced numerical analyst or mathematical physicist winces when he sees a system of linear algebraic equations. He knows from long and bitter experience how many traps exist in this area, even for the wary.

Similarly, the task of using a solution of an equation that involves Fourier series, or orthogonal series in general, is a major one. Much of nineteenth-century analysis, the theory of the transformation of series and summability of series, centered around the theme of using slowly converging or diverging series to obtain accurate numerical solutions. When ten thousand terms of a series are required to obtain two or three significant figures, it cannot be assumed that we possess an effective solution. Some of the most famous transformation formulas we know, such as the Poisson transformation formula or the Euler summation formulas, were developed for numerical purposes. It is also interesting to realize that a formula originally proposed for these purposes, the Watson-Sommerfeld transformation, has led to an exciting development in modern physics, the theory of Regge poles, or polology as it is sometimes called.

One reason that the question of summation of series has assumed a less important role than formerly is the fact that we now possess simpler means for attacking the original differential equation if numerical values are desired.

Without delving further into the history of mathematical analysis, we can assert that the problem of using explicit analytic solutions of equations, or the equations themselves, to obtain numerical results is one of the dominant themes of eighteenth and nineteenth century mathematics.

We are now faced with a discontinuity in intellectual history, the digital computer, which completely changes our ability to do arithmetic and to obtain numbers. Therefore, we can predict confidently that it will have an overwhelming effect on mathematical analysis. The emphasis will shift from ingenuity in the small to ingenuity in the large. Perhaps an appropriate analogy is afforded by the influence of analytic geometry on synthetic geometry. A great deal of intellectual challenge leaves an area when we know that we possess a direct method for solving a particular problem. The beauty remains, as it does in synthetic geometry, but it is no longer a vital research area.

It has often been pointed out in philosophy that a significant change in quantity results in a change in quality.

6. Parallelization and Miniaturization

Paradoxically, the contemporary computer is probably the most inefficient machine in history. A roomful of equipment can do only one arithmetic operation at a time.

The big new direction in computers designed to remedy this situation is "parallelization." This term stands for the design of computers of hybrid type, both digital and analog, that will contain different components, or subcomputers, carrying out different operations simultaneously. Parallelization is part of the trend toward self-organizing computers. Add this development, which is at most five years off, to "miniaturization," which means cheaper and more rapid computers with great increase in storage capacity, and we can begin to think in terms of amplification factors for arithmetic processing of orders of 10^{18} and more.

This thought staggers the imagination. When we contemplate the numerical solution of three-dimensional partial differential equations in a matter of minutes, we begin to have some idea of the new world of physics and engineering that the computer has opened up.

Again, let me point out that although we can now do many problems quickly and simply that could not be done at all previously and others very much faster than before, vast classes of problems still remain that at the moment are completely beyond any routine approach with the computer. In the fields of statistical mechanics and quantum field theory, to name just a couple, there is little danger of the computer's putting either the mathematician or the mathematical physicist out of jobs.

Even in fields where the mathematician can now routinely obtain solutions, there is the goal already mentioned of reducing the mathematical level of the algorithms used. Furthermore, there is always a strong possibility that a reformulation of a known process may lead us to a new view of the unknown. At the very least, interesting new mathematical problems arise in this fashion.

Obviously, "business as usual" cannot continue in the universities. Whether or not we want to, we must examine the kind of research being done and the courses being taught to see whether they make sense in the micro-microsecond multiplication world.

7. A Simple Trajectory Process and Classical Imbedding

At this point, you may well demand that it is about time that I cease this philosophizing and provide some examples of what I have been discussing. In defense of my procrastination and verbal meandering, I claim that the examples themselves would carry little weight if the objective were not clearly limned.

The first example I present was not first chronologically. Unfortunately, chronological origins and logical origins seldom overlap, which causes considerable difficulties in teaching a subject or presenting it in book form. If the subject is presented in some logical order, the student has difficulty understanding where the ideas arose. Only the history of the subject shows that, but history is seldom suitable for preliminary pedagogy. Even the professional historian finds it difficult to portray the spirit of the times, the ideas that were half formed in many minds. The teacher is usually caught between his desire to present a subject both intuitively and rigorously. Enough of apologies.

Suppose that I throw a strone straight up with velocity v. Assuming a flat earth and no atmosphere, I ask the question, "How high does the stone go?" The mathematician has an elegant approach to answer questions of this nature. To answer this specific question, he proposes to imbed the original question within a family of questions. The classical imbedding is to determine the height of the stone at time t. This step is basic in providing an approach to this problem requiring only elementary calculus.

Almost all textbooks in mechanics, mathematical physics, and so on are somewhat misleading because they do not explicitly point out that this imbedding is a very ingenious idea, a philosophical concept of great sophistication. The assumption tacitly exists that this kind of imbedding is automatic, the kind of mathematical method that would occur to anyone asked the question. Of course, this assumption is hardly true.

The student must be taught that a powerful approach to the solution of a particular problem is to imbed it within a family of problems. This approach is used across the intellectual board, from comparative anatomy to comparative religion.

Once this principle has been grasped, the operational problem is to find the appropriate family of problems. If I can sufficiently emphasize the point that it is to be expected that there will always be several ways of imbedding, I will have communicated the essence of this chapter. The rest is entertainment (at least I hope so) and perhaps some associated edification.

Corollary to the foregoing is the fact that the classical formulations of mathematical physics were not inscribed on the tablet that Moses carried away from Mount Sinai. Nor did Prometheus steal them from the gods when he stole the fire. They were created by mortal men. Too many people sincerely believe that Newton's equations or Maxwell's equations or, more recently, the Schrodinger equation, are gospel. On the other hand, they feel equally certain that the fellow down the hall trying valiantly to cope with the complexities of biology or plasticity or economic systems is merely constructing "mathematical models." Not "truth," mind you, merely mathematical approximations.

Every mathematical formulation, of course, is to be considered an approximation, designed for some particular purposes and with some experimental data and numerical techniques in mind. Whoever believes that there are irrevocably true equations describing the universe is better equipped intellectually to watch TV espionage series than to engage in serious scientific endeavors.

As I have constantly emphasized, once the digital computer sprang into existence from the foreheads of mathematicians like

Athena from the forehead of Zeus, no formulation of a scientific theory could henceforth remain sacred. Regardless of the parentage and the lineage, it became necessary to ask, "Is this formulation really satisfactory?" Some people feel that this kind of critical examination of classical equations is disloyal to the memory of Euler or Gauss, or Laplace or Lagrange. Imbued with ancestor worship, they want to keep everything the way it was when giants roamed the earth. I say that to be really loyal to the spirits of Euler and Gauss, one should do what they would have done had they had a digital computer to work with. You can be sure that they would have been busily reformulating theories in such a way as to take maximum advantage of this remarkable tool.

Let me pursue the classical imbedding technique.[4] We replace the original question of determining the maximum height by asking for the height at an arbitrary time t. If we can answer this general question, presumably we can answer the original query. One difficulty of this approach is that the original proponent of the question is apt to complain, both querulously and plaintively, that he doesn't care where the stone is at a general time t. He may well feel that he asked a simple question and received a complicated answer.[5] He doesn't want to know that much. The mathematician can only shrug his shoulders and reply that this is the only method he knows and that, furthermore, the additional information is occasionally useful. The second part of his reply is true; the first part is not, as we shall see.

The first step in the solution process consists of an imbedding within a family of problems. The second step consists of finding relations between various members of this family. In this fashion, we hope to pass by simple steps from the known to the unknown. Specifically, in this case we wish to connect the height at time t with the height at time $t + \Delta$, where Δ is small. One reason to do this is our knowledge of the location of the stone at time zero, namely on the ground. Let $u(t)$ denote the height at time t.

In the limit as $\Delta \to 0$, this relation between the heights at time t and $t + \Delta$ becomes a differential equation, one of the fundamental mathematical tools of science. To derive this equation for $u(t)$

---

[4] This time I mean it!

[5] To which the philosopher retorts, "Why shouldn't a simple question have a complicated answer?" See chapter 3 for a further discussion of this point.

directly, we proceed as follows. Let the mass of the stone, considered as a point particle, be unity and let the acceleration due to gravity be denoted by $-g$. Then using the relation $f = ma$, force is equal to mass times acceleration, we have the differential equation

$$u'' = -g. \tag{1}$$

This is a second-order differential equation, and fortunately we have two initial conditions to go along with it,

$$u(0) = 0, \; u'(0) = v, \tag{2}$$

corresponding to the circumstances that the stone was on the ground at the initial time and thrown upwards with velocity v.

From Eq. 1 and 2, it is simple to obtain the desired behavior of $u(t)$ as a function of time, namely

$$u(t) = vt - \frac{gt^2}{2}. \tag{3}$$

The maximum height is obtained by first finding the time at which this height is attained. Setting the derivative of $u(t)$ equal to zero to obtain this time, we have

$$0 = u'(t) = v - gt,$$
$$t_{\max} = \frac{v}{g}. \tag{4}$$

Hence, using Eq. 3,

$$u_{\max} = \frac{v^2}{2g}. \tag{5}$$

8. Realism and Operational Aspects

The mathematician is justifiably pleased with this fine textbook example. What happens, however, when important physical effects such as air resistance are included in the mathematical model? The simple differential equation of Eq. 7.1 is replaced by an equation of the form

$$u'' = g(u, u'), \tag{1}$$

which, in general, cannot be integrated in explicit analytic terms. If $t_{\max}$ and $u_{\max}$ are desired, numerical integration is required, starting with the initial conditions $u(0) = h$, $u'(0) = v$. As long as we are carrying out numerical calculations, we may as well consider the more general case where the initial elevation is h (Figure 10).

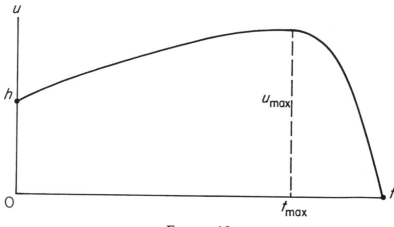

FIGURE 10

With the aid of the numerical solution, t_{max} and u_{max} can be determined. Suppose that we want the same data for another situation involving a different h and v. Then another numerical integration of the differential equation is required. This procedure is not much of a chore in this case, but consider how inefficient it is. In order to obtain one number, the maximum height, we must calculate $u(t)$ for a range of values. If the maximum altitude is desired for a different initial velocity or initial height, another numerical integration over the entire range is required.

In most engineering and physical investigations the dependence of the final result on certain parameters, such as initial conditions, is what is urgently required. A specific answer is not desired so much as a set of answers, a *sensitivity analysis*. In the foregoing case, what we want, then, is

$$u_{max} = f(h, v), \tag{2}$$

which is to say, we want the dependence of the maximum height on the initial elevation and the initial velocity.

Can we find $f(h, v)$ directly without abstracting these functional values from a set of calculations for the function $u(t) \equiv u(t, h, v)$?

9. A Multistage Process

To present the basic idea of a new approach that affirmatively answers the foregoing question, let us consider the simpler equation of Sec. 7 first. This equation corresponds to the trajectory process where a stone is thrown straight up through a homogeneous atmosphere, in this case a vacuum (Figure 11).

We begin by observing that this may be considered to be a multistage process—not a multistage decision process, but multistage all the same. Suppose that the stone starts at 0 with velocity v and attains the maximum altitude OR. Let a time Δ transpire, where Δ is a small quantity. In this time interval, the stone attains a height $v\Delta$, the distance OP ignoring higher-order terms in Δ. Furthermore, at P the upward velocity is $v - g\Delta$, again ignoring higher-order terms (Figure 12).

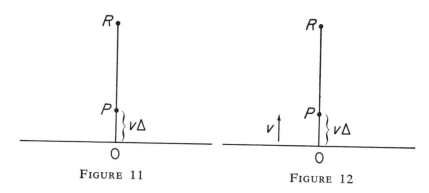

FIGURE 11   FIGURE 12

We now make the important observation that the maximum additional altitude attained starting at P with velocity $v - g\Delta$ is PR. From this simple fact, we can readily obtain the desired functional dependence. Let

$$f(v) = \text{the maximum additional altitude attained starting} \quad (1)$$
$$\text{with velocity } v.$$

Then $OR = v\Delta + PR$ translates into the functional equation

$$f(v) = v\Delta + f(v - g\Delta) + 0(\Delta^2). \quad (2)$$

Writing

$$f(v - g\Delta) = f(v) - g\Delta f'(v) + 0(\Delta^2), \quad (3)$$

we have

$$f'(v) = \frac{v}{g} + 0(\Delta^2), \tag{4}$$

whence, in the limit as $\Delta \to 0$, we obtain the differential equation

$$f'(v) = \frac{v}{g}. \tag{5}$$

The initial condition is clearly $f(0) = 0$. Hence, the solution is

$$f(v) = \frac{v^2}{2g}. \tag{6}$$

This result should make an impression on you. It clearly exhibits the fact that it may be possible in carefully chosen situations to obtain some desired data without the necessity of tabulating all possible information. Observe that this method does not tell us where the stone is at time t. But we may not care for this data at the moment.

This is an example of a new kind of imbedding, the theory of invariant imbedding. The analogy between the procedure followed in chapter 1 in applying dynamic programming to the calculus of variations is not accidental. Indeed, the method followed here is patterned after that used previously. Presumably, a theory of multistage processes should precede a theory of multistage decision processes. It just didn't happen that way, which is consistent with my remark that historical development need not be logical.

10. Air Resistance

Let us now see what happens when we apply the same technique to the determination of the function defined in Eq. 8.2, the maximum altitude attained traveling through an inhomogeneous atmosphere. Referring to Figure 13, we see that the maximum additional altitude gained from P depends on both the velocity at P and the height OP already attained, inasmuch as we have assumed an inhomogeneous atmosphere. Let us then draw a new figure, Figure 13. Introduce the function[6]

[6] Why don't we introduce the simpler function $f(v)$ as before? The answer is that we tried this and it doesn't work. We don't seem to be able to obtain an equation directly for this function. This is an example of what I pointed out before, namely that the proper imbedding is not always obvious. Some experimentation is always required when a new type of problem appears.

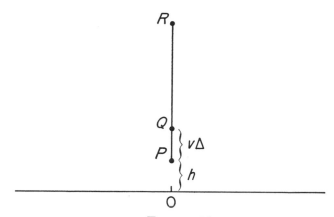

FIGURE 13

$$f(h, v) = \max_t u(t), \tag{1}$$

where u is determined by

$$u'' = g(u, u'), \; u(0) = h, \; u'(0) = v. \tag{2}$$

Then the relation $PR = v\Delta + QR$ translates into

$$f(h, v) = v\Delta + f(h + v\Delta, v + g(h, v)\Delta) + 0(\Delta^2). \tag{3}$$

In the limit as $\Delta \to 0$ this becomes the partial differential equation

$$0 = v + vfh + g(h, v)fv, \tag{4}$$

with the initial condition

$$f(h, 0) = h, \tag{5}$$

for $h \geqq 0$.

In general this equation will require numerical techniques for its solution. In this case, we can employ the method of characteristics or use Eq. 3 directly. But the important point is that now every bit of information obtained is useful information as far as the original question is concerned. Every value of $f(h, v)$ is the answer to a specific problem. Once again, we obtain no information concerning the position of the stone at a general time t.

11. One-dimensional Neutron Transport Theory

Let us now turn to a more important example illustrating the use of alternative imbedding techniques, a simple version of a one-

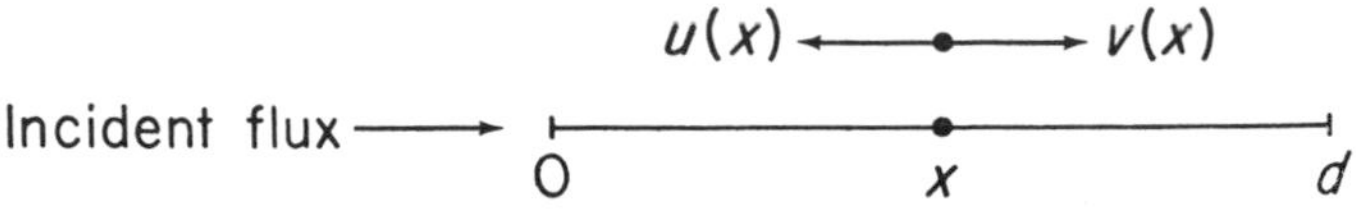

$$u(x) \longleftarrow \bullet \longrightarrow v(x)$$

Incident flux $\longrightarrow$ |————————————•————————————|
　　　　　　　　　　　O　　　　　　　　　　　x　　　　　　　　　　d

FIGURE 14

dimensional neutron transport process. Consider a one-dimensional rod, as indicated in Figure 14, and suppose that point particles, which we can think of as neutrons, can traverse the rod in either direction. As these neutrons travel through the rod, there is the possibility of an interaction with the constituents of the rod. When an interaction occurs, the original neutron disappears and is replaced by two others, one moving to the right and one to the left. This is a simple model of nuclear fission.

Assuming that there is a unit incident flux of neutrons at one end, as indicated above, we want to determine the reflected and transmitted fluxes. The classical imbedding is to consider the more general problem of determining the internal fluxes, the left-hand and right-hand flux at an arbitrary point x inside the rod. Let $u(x)$ denote the left-hand flux at x and $v(x)$ the right-hand flux. If we can determine those quantities for a general position of x, we can determine $u(0)$ and $v(d)$ and thus the required reflected and transmitted fluxes.

In order to treat the process by means of differential equations, we make some simplifying assumptions. We suppose that when a neutron passes through an infinitesimal length Δ in either direction at any location in the rod there is a probability $(1 - p\Delta)$ of no interaction and a probability $p\Delta$ that fission will occur. Since our fluxes will be expected fluxes, this is equivalent to the statement that a fraction, $(1 - p\Delta)$, of the neutrons pass through the interval of length Δ with no interaction, and a fraction $p\Delta$ undergo fission. As mentioned, when fission occurs, one neutron goes to the left and one to the right.

To derive a set of differential equations satisfied by $u(x)$ and

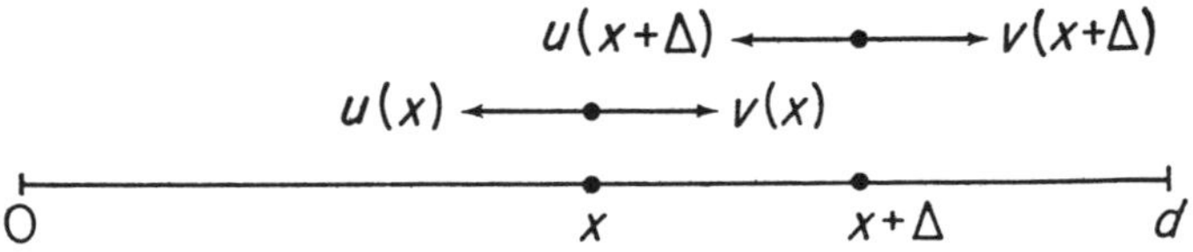

$$u(x+\Delta) \longleftarrow \bullet \longrightarrow v(x+\Delta)$$
$$u(x) \longleftarrow \bullet \longrightarrow v(x)$$

|————————————————•————————•————————|
O　　　　　　　　　　　　　　x　　　　　x+\Delta　　　　d

FIGURE 15

$v(x)$, we employ a familiar bookkeeping technique. Consider Figure 15. The flux to the left at x is a consequence of the flux at $x + \Delta$ which manages to traverse $[x + \Delta, x]$ without interaction, together with the consequences of interactions in $[x, x + \Delta]$ due to $u(x + \Delta)$ and $v(x)$. Writing this out, we have

$$u(x) = (1 - p\,\Delta)u(x + \Delta) + p\,\Delta u(x + \Delta) + p\,\Delta v(x), \qquad (1)$$

ignoring additional interactions which produce terms that are $0(\Delta^2)$. Similarly,

$$v(x) = (1 - p\,\Delta)v(x - \Delta) + p\,\Delta v(x - \Delta) + p\,\Delta u(x). \qquad (2)$$

Writing

$$\begin{aligned} u(x + \Delta) &= u(x) + \Delta u'(x), \\ v(x - \Delta) &= v(x) - \Delta v'(x), \end{aligned} \qquad (3)$$

simplifying Eq. 1 and 2, and passing to the limit as $\Delta \to 0$, we obtain the system of linear differential equations

$$\begin{aligned} u'(x) &= -pv(x), \\ v'(x) &= pu(x), \end{aligned} \qquad (4)$$

with the two-point boundary conditions

$$v(0) = 1, \quad u(d) = 0. \qquad (5)$$

There is little difficulty in obtaining the explicit analytic solution,

$$\begin{aligned} u(x) &= \frac{\sin p(x - d)}{\cos pd}, \\ v(x) &= \frac{\cos p(x - d)}{\cos pd}. \end{aligned} \qquad (6)$$

This shows that the "critical length" is $l_c = \pi/2p$, and

$$u(0) = \tan pd, \quad v(d) = \sec pd. \qquad (7)$$

12. Alternate Imbedding

Suppose the problem is to construct a shield for a nuclear reactor. In particular, suppose we are interested primarily in determining the intensity of reflected and transmitted flux as a function of the thickness and that we have no interest in the internal flux. Can we obtain differential equations for these quantities as functions of the thickness?

Introduce a new variable, y, as the length of the one-dimensional rod and write

$$r(y) = \text{the intensity of reflected flux from a rod of length} \atop y \text{ due to a unit incident flux.} \qquad (1)$$

This is an imbedding very different from that of Sec. 11. Yet it is a very natural one from the standpoint of the engineer or experimental physicist. One member of this new family of problems has a very simple solution, namely

$$r(0) = 0. \qquad (2)$$

To obtain a relation connecting $r(y)$ with $r(y - \Delta)$, we argue as follows. Consider Figure 16. The flux incident at y traverses the

Incident flux $\longrightarrow$ |⊢————————————|————————————————————|
                      y $y-\Delta$ O

FIGURE 16

infinitesimal length $[y, y - \Delta]$ with the following possibilities of interaction and noninteraction. The interaction produces an immediate reflected flux of $p\Delta$ together with the intensity due to the reflection from the remaining length $[y - \Delta, 0]$. This contribution is $p\Delta r(y - \Delta)$.[7] All further contributions due to this flux passing through $[y - \Delta, y]$ are $0(\Delta^2)$ and can thus be ignored.

The intensity of flux incident upon $y - \Delta$ as a result of no interaction in $[y, y - \Delta]$ is $(1 - p\Delta)$. The immediate reflected intensity is $(1 - p\Delta)r(y - \Delta)$. In passing through $[y - \Delta, y]$, it is reduced to $(1 - p\Delta)^2 r(y - \Delta)$, with a fraction $p\Delta$ engaging in interaction producing an additional contribution of

$$(1 - p\Delta)r(y - \Delta)[p\Delta + p\Delta r(y - \Delta)]. \qquad (3)$$

The first term is the result of neutrons going directly to the left as the result of fission, and the second is the result of reflection of neutrons going to the right as a result of fission. Adding together all the contributions, we obtain

[7] The contributions to the left-hand flux at y are, of course, made at different times. However, this is of no import here inasmuch as we are considering only the steady-state process.

$$r(y) = [p\Delta + p\Delta r(y - \Delta)] + (1 - p\Delta)^2 r(y - \Delta)$$
$$+ (1 - p\Delta)r(y - \Delta)[p\Delta + p\Delta r(y - \Delta)] + O(\Delta^2). \tag{4}$$

Writing $r(y - \Delta) = r(y) - \Delta r'(y)$, the foregoing yields after simplification and passage to the limit the equation

$$r'(y) = p + pr(y)^2, \tag{5}$$

with the initial condition of Eq. 2.

The solution is

$$r(y) = \tan py, \tag{6}$$

agreeing with the result of Sec. 11.

13. Multigroup, Multidimensional Version

Both of the foregoing imbedding techniques can readily be extended to the case where the neutrons possess both energy and direction. Introducing both discrete energy levels and discrete angles, the classical approach leads to a coupled system of linear vector differential equations

$$x' = Ax + By, \quad x(0) = c,$$
$$y' = Cx + Dy, \quad y(T) = 0, \tag{1}$$

while the second approach leads to a vector Riccati differential equation of the form

$$R' = A + BR + RC + RDR, \quad R(0) = 0. \tag{2}$$

The significance of these two formulations will be discussed later. Meanwhile, let me point out that in Sec. 12, I employed what is called a "particle-counting" technique to obtain the equation for $r(y)$. This procedure is important for many reasons, not the least of which is the fact that it shows the physical significance of each term. There are, however, direct ways of obtaining Eq. 12.5 from Eq. 11.4 without the intervention of any physical concepts.

14. Los Alamos and the Atomic Bomb

Now that I hope the reader is reasonably convinced that there are opportunities to use a novel approach of the foregoing type in mathematical physics, let me pause a moment and describe some of the origins of the underlying ideas. As usual with my entry into various fields of mathematics, my interest in these matters developed accidentally. During the war (World War II, as it is now necessary to say in order to identify it uniquely), I was fortunate to be stationed at Los Alamos for the time that I was nominally in the Army, a member of the Special Engineering Division.[8] As a member of the Theoretical Division, I worked for Robert Marshak (now a distinguished Meson physicist) on problems concerned with various aspects of neutron transport processes. These problems presumably had something to do with the construction of the atomic bomb. Why I say "presumably" will be discussed in a moment.

It is important for my tale that I mention that the mathematical problems encountered in this area are very close to those encountered in the study of radiative transfer. In neutron transport theory, we want to know what happens to neutrons as they penetrate a material; how they are scattered, reflected, absorbed; what the consequences of fission are, and so forth. In radiative transfer, we wish to study similar problems connected with various types of fluxes penetrating terrestrial and planetary atmospheres. The equations ordinarily used to describe these different kinds of physical phenomena are of identical form. There is, of course, the significant difference that in neutron transport there is a fission process, fortunately not present in ordinary scattering processes.

The mathematical methods used at Los Alamos in 1944 to 1945 were understandably neither very effective nor very efficient in dealing with the integro-differential equations of transport theory. The digital computer at Los Alamos was considered a wonder because it was reputed to be able to solve up to ten simultaneous linear differential equations. I do not know whether it ever did anything that spectacular in 1944 or 1945. In any case, the computer had two slaves, two master sergeants, who slept in a room next to it. One of these vassals was required to be available for repair and maintenance at all times. The bulk of numerical work, however, was done by hand, by vast teams of people called "computers." I even did some of this work for twenty-four hours in order to get an idea of what was involved. Then I struck for better

[8] It is pleasant to note that my research efforts got me promoted first to Staff Sergeant and then to Civilian, the best rank of all.

working conditions, or at least more interesting ones. But that is another story. There is nothing like a few hours of grinding numerical toil to make one appreciate a modern digital computer.

In any case, we saw that large-scale computational efforts could not be undertaken under these situations. Consequently, all kinds of ingenious analytic approximations based on physical intuition were made in order to obtain some numbers to give to the bomb designers to aid them in their efforts.

Sometimes one sees the comment that the construction of the atomic bomb was a triumph of mathematical analysis. Furthermore, as an exercise in cultural history, one can trace the rise in esteem (and even more important, in pay) of the mathematician with the diffusion of this propaganda through the public ranks. Actually, an operational atomic bomb was a triumph of scientific and engineering genius. The people who were really responsible for the success of the effort were men such as Fermi, Bethe, Ulam, von Neumann, Szilard, Wigner, Bohr, Alvarez, and Oppenheimer (to mention only a few), some of the foremost physicists and mathematical physicists of the time. When you have people of this level of brilliance working on engineering problems, you do very well, with or without computers.

The mathematics involved was highly unreliable, both because of the simplifying analytical approximations required to get numbers, as I have mentioned, and perhaps even more because the basic physics was very shaky. As far as the physical theories were concerned, in connection with pressure, temperature, and energy, we were working in ranges far outside known theory or known experimental results. Similarly, the times of interest, microseconds and tenths of microseconds, were much smaller than those encountered in any previous electronic efforts. Furthermore, the sensitivity of the efficiency of the bomb to the synchronization of these times was remarkable.

That an atomic bomb could be built sometime was clear to everyone after some preliminary orientation. That it could be built rapidly and effectively enough to be used against the Nazis (who were believed to be engaged in large-scale efforts of this nature themselves) was not at all clear. That it was used against the Japanese people rather than against the German military machine was a source of sadness to all the scientific personnel involved. That it ended the war against Japan without a land invasion was a strong consolation.

For about a year and a half at Los Alamos, I devoted my time and efforts to studying various simple approximations connected with neutron transport theory devised by Marshak, Fermi, and others. In so doing, I developed a healthy respect for the formidable difficulties that physicists and engineers face in trying to use mathematical analysis in some fruitful fashion, and for the many ingenious ways in which they triumph over major obstacles. In particular, I began to appreciate the many advantages in the mathematical analysis of an equation that could be gained from a thorough understanding of the underlying physical process.

I came to realize the great difference between the aims and ambitions of the scientist and those of the mathematician. To paraphrase a well-known witticism, I might say that the mathematicians and physicists are two groups divided by the use of a common language, mathematics.

It was easy to observe how primitive were the mathematical methods used in neutron transport and how frustrating was research in this area for lack of powerful numerical techniques. Consequently, when the book by S. Chandrasekhar on the subject of radiative transfer appeared in 1956, I was very curious to see what, if anything, had been done in ten years to overcome the many obstacles in the path of scientific understanding. In thumbing through this elegant work, I was entranced to see several chapters devoted to "Principles of Invariance." By this time, I had been working in the theory of dynamic programming for almost ten years, with the result that I was well sensitized to invariance concepts and to multistage processes.

As I indicated in chapter 1, the basic idea of dynamic programming is "invariance," the fact that at each stage of the decision process one faces the same kind of problem over the remaining time period. With this conceptual set, I looked at Chandrasekhar's work and realized that the principles of invariance were applications of the basic ideas of dynamic programming, without, however, the associated optimization. This, of course, made for considerable simplification.

15. Ambarzumian and Principles of Invariance

Stimulated by this, Robert Kalaba and I looked into the formulation of Chandrasekhar in more detail and discovered that, as usual with physicists, there was a great deal of physical insight and ingenuity associated with a modest mathematical training. What was needed was a more intensive and extensive mathematical formulation in order to apply the full power of the simple and fundamental ideas both in the world of science and in classical analysis.

Of course, there is always a big difference between saying that an idea is simple after it is well known and well analyzed and first discerning it among a thousand alternate fuzzy concepts. As many people have observed, hindsight is 20–20. Consequently, too much credit cannot be given to the brilliance of Ambarzumian, the Russian astrophysicist, who first introduced these principles of invariance into astrophysics. By all means, I want to emphasize the magnitude of his contribution. Although fragments of the basic idea can be traced in a number of papers of the nineteenth century, Ambarzumian was the first to exploit it in a really meaningful fashion. His work stimulated Chandrasekhar who, in equally brilliant fashion, applied it intensively and greatly extended its scope.

Ambarzumian, like many other physicists of the time, was concerned with the following problem: How does light propagate through the atmosphere? This problem was much too difficult for the time (and far from any satisfactory form even today). Hence,

FIGURE 17

he contented himself, as the others did, with the following simplified
version of the process.

Suppose that you have a plane-parallel atmosphere with incident
fluxes as indicated in Figure 17. Given an incident flux of known
intensity at angle θ at one boundary of an atmosphere, what is the
intensity of the reflected flux at angle ϕ?

16. Classical Imbedding

The classical approach to this problem involves imbedding. In
order to determine the reflected flux, we consider the family of
problems connected with the determination of the flux in an arbitrary direction at an arbitrary point within the medium. This is the
usual approach of mathematical physics in process after process, as
we have already indicated.

In order to obtain relations between the answers to individual
questions in this family of problems, we use conservation principles.
We consider an infinitesimal region inside the domain and assert,
quite plausibly, that what comes out is a result of what comes in,
together with the consequences of interactions in the region. In this
case, we allow only absorption, together with scattering and rera-
diation. (See Figure 18.)

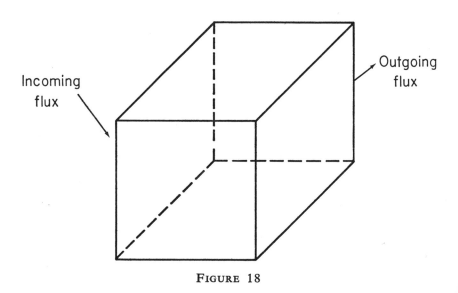

FIGURE 18

The equation obtained by this simple accounting device is called the transport equation. Depending upon how ambitious we are, the equation can be made linear or nonlinear. If we consider interactions between elements in the flux plus interaction of the flux with the medium, the classical Boltzmann equation is obtained. If we consider only interaction of the flux with the medium and add the proviso that the properties of the medium are not affected by the flux, linear equations are derived. Fortunately, in radiative transfer and in neutron transport theory, a great deal can be done on the basis of linear models. On the other hand, hydrodynamics requires nonlinear equations, as does the study of lasers.

For the plane-parallel atmosphere of Sec. 15, under suitable assumptions of homogeneity and isotropy, plus stationarity, we obtain the deceptively simple equation

$$\mu \frac{\partial I}{\partial \tau}(\tau, \mu) - \sigma I(\tau, \mu) = B(\tau) + \frac{c}{2} \int_{-1}^{1} I(\tau, \mu') d\mu', \tag{1}$$

with the initial condition $I(0, -\mu) = 0, I(0, +\mu) = 0, 0 < \mu < 1$. The boundary conditions vary depending on the presence of internal sources, as above, or of external flux. The function $B(\tau)$ depends on the type of internal sources that are present.

It is hard to believe that an equation with this appearance could contain so much lurking difficulty, but it does—fortunately for the growth of mathematical analysis.

17. Associated Analysis

It is interesting to note that the celebrated Wiener-Hopf equation came into analysis by way of a simple transformation of Eq. 16.1. More recently, distribution theory, functional analysis, and singular integral equations have all been successfully applied to its study. Elegant as all these methods are, they suffer from two serious defects as far as the scientist is concerned. They require a high level of analytic training for successful utilization; and, perhaps what is worse, the methods developed for the simple process described above do not readily carry over to the study of inhomogeneous, anisotropic media, nor to the multigroup[9] or time-dependent cases.

Let me note further in passing that one reason for considerable

---

[9] That is, many-velocity or energy-dependent.

difficulty in any straightforward computational approach is the inherent numerical instability of Eq. 16.1. Since μ can assume values between $+1$ and -1, it turns out that any routine discretization of Eq. 16.1 leads to a system of linear differential equations subject to two-point boundary conditions in which half the characteristic roots are positive and half are negative with a large variation in magnitude. This is analogous to the problem encountered in using the Euler equation, where a similar unstable situation occurs.

18. Ambarzumian's Approach

Ambarzumian was familiar with both the classical formulation and the classical difficulties. He decided to try an entirely different approach based on the use of observables. Suppose we say that we don't care at all what goes on inside the atmosphere but want to concentrate our attention on what is directly measurable, the reflected flux. We have prepared the path for this approach in Sec. 12.

Quantum mechanics has made the idea of an observable very fashionable and simultaneously has attached a certain degree of odium to "hidden variables." The only difficulty with fashionable philosophy is that it soon ceases to be philosophy and turns into fetish. Philosophy is to be used when it is helpful and discarded when it is not. Hence, I am willing to think solely in terms of observables if a useful formulation can be obtained in this way. If not, I am willing to introduce some nonobservables. After all, one generation's hidden variables can easily be the next generation's observables.

An elegant formulation is desirable, and to that end Occam's razor should be ruthlessly applied. Can we get by with observables in the present case, which is to say, can we obtain an equation that directly furnishes the reflected flux? To this end, introduce the function

$$f(\theta,\phi) = \text{the intensity of reflected flux in direction } \phi \text{ from a} \qquad (1)$$
$$\text{semi-infinite atmosphere as a consequence of plane-}$$
$$\text{parallel incident flux in direction } \theta \text{ of unit intensity.}$$

This function translates into mathematical language the statement that the intensity of reflected flux depends upon the two angles

θ and ϕ. However, as pointed out, defining the function does not necessarily mean that we can obtain an equation for it.

Ambarzumian's idea was very ingenious. Consider Figure 19.

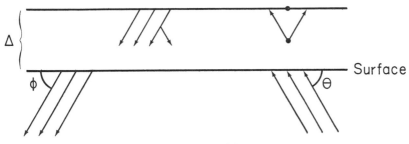

FIGURE 19

What happens when the incident flux hits the surface of the atmosphere? It must first penetrate a layer of thickness Δ, which we consider to be small. An individual particle can traverse this layer without interaction with the medium, or it can interact, resulting in absorption and scattering. If Δ is small, we can assume that at most one interaction can occur in this layer. As in the one-dimensional case, subsequent interactions produce contributions that are $0(\Delta^2)$.

The particles that traverse the first layer, with or without interaction, are incident upon the second interface at certain angles. Now, the point of Ambarzumian's argument is that these particles face the same kind of successive interaction process faced originally by the particles incident at the first interface.

Removal of a layer of thickness Δ from a semi-infinite medium leaves a semi-infinite medium. In symbols,

$$\infty - \Delta = \infty. \tag{2}$$

This expresses the invariance of an infinite process.

Hence, we can write the reflected flux from the second interface in terms of the function f introduced in Eq. 1. Thus there is no need to inquire explicitly as to what goes on inside the second semi-infinite region. This reflected flux can in turn pass through the Δ-layer without interaction, or it can be scattered, resulting in some contribution to the total reflected flux and to another flux incident at the second interface. The result may again be expressed in terms of the function f. Similarly, the incident flux passing through the

Δ-layer may be scattered, resulting in a direct contribution to the total reflected flux and to a flux incident on the second interface. No further interactions need be considered if Δ is considered to be an infinitesimal. A simple analysis shows that their contributions are $0(\Delta^2)$.

Passing to the limit as $\Delta \to 0$, we obtain in this fashion a quadratically nonlinear integral equation

$$\frac{1}{\lambda}\left(\frac{1}{u}+\frac{1}{v}\right) R(v, u) = \left[1 + \frac{1}{2}\int_0^1 R(w, u)\frac{dw}{w}\right]\left[1 + \frac{1}{2}\int_0^1 R(v, z)\frac{dz}{z}\right]. \quad (3)$$

Here $u = \cos \theta$, $v = \cos \phi$.

Using a transformation based on physical intuition, this equation can be reduced to an integral equation for a function of one variable,

$$f(u) = 1 + \frac{\lambda}{2}\int_0^1 \frac{uf(u)f(v)dv}{u + v}. \quad (4)$$

Even in the days before digital computers, this equation was in a form suitable for numerical solution. What is needed is a dedicated calculator (or equivalently, some graduate students), together with the use of quadrature techniques to be described later. Extensive calculations were carried out by Ambarzumian and Chandrasekhar.

19. Ingenuity versus Training

One great merit of the approach of Ambarzumian and Chandrasekhar was to replace the linear transport equation by a nonlinear integral equation of Fredholm type that was more amenable to numerical solution, despite the nonlinearity. Yet a continuation of this approach led to serious difficulties. To some extent what they did was a reflection of the times; to some extent it was a reflection on the mathematical training of the scientist.

In studying certain aspects of radiative transfer, we start out with a semi-infinite atmosphere, presumably because it is easier to work with and, by the ingenious methods of Ambarzumian and Chandrasekhar, it is easier to obtain numerical and analytic results. Of course, real atmospheres are not semi-infinite, nor are they plane-parallel. Ignoring the latter point for the moment, let us concentrate on the more realistic assumption of an atmosphere of finite thickness.

As it turns out, a clever modification of the invariance trick used in the semi-infinite case enables us to handle the case of finite thickness. By subtracting a layer at the bottom interface and adding an equal layer at the top interface, we can obtain a set of coupled Fredholm integral equations for determining transmitted and reflected fluxes. This approach is difficult because integral equations of this nature do not lend themselves well to numerical solution by digital computer. The difficulties increase as realistic features such as anisotropy are added; and, of course, a new calculation is required for each different thickness.

When we turn to spherical and cylindrical atmospheres, we find that the methods break down completely. The astrophysicist is now left to rely on his own ingenuity.

At this point it is appropriate to comment on the mathematical abilities, thus the mathematical models, of scientists in general. A principal characteristic of a top scientist is that he generally is mathematically talented but not mathematically trained. In other words, he is an amateur at mathematical analysis. There is nothing pejorative about this; it is a fact.

This ingenuousness often is useful in the small and even in the large. Fundamentally new approaches have been developed by researchers blissfully unaware of the well-worn path of standard theory, but such instances are rare. On the whole, a *tour de force* results in a *cul de sac*. With this fact in mind, the mathematical formulations of physical processes by biologists, economists, engineers, and physicists should be considered, not with awe, but with skepticism.

This situation prevails particularly today, when the development of the digital computer permits the mathematician to pick and choose from a number of alternate formulations. Indeed, one primary function of the mathematician is to educate the scientist in the use of these different methods and their advantages and disadvantages.

Although the digital computer is poorly equipped to solve boundary-value problems, it is particularly suited to solve initial-value problems because their solution requires repetitive operations. Can we reformulate, therefore, much of mathematical physics in terms of initial-value problems? It turns out that we can.

20. Invariant Imbedding

To obtain an analytic formulation that is well suited to the abilities of the digital computer, let us imbed the problem of determining the reflected flux from a plane-parallel layer of specified thickness within a family of such problems where the thickness of the layer is a parameter that can assume any value from zero up. We know the solution to the problem of zero thickness in a trivial fashion (Figure 20).

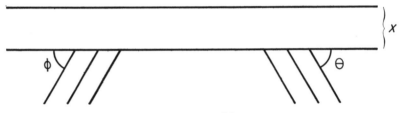

FIGURE 20

We regard the intensity of reflected flux at angle ϕ as a function of the incident angle θ, the reflected angle ϕ and the thickness x, denoted by $r(\theta, \phi, x)$. To obtain an equation for this function, we argue as before, using Figure 21. In place of the symbolic relation

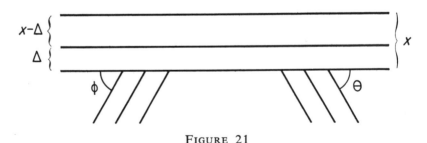

FIGURE 21

of Eq. 18.2, we use the relation

$$x - \Delta = (x - \Delta). \tag{1}$$

This relation enables us to connect the functions $r(\theta, \phi, x)$ and $r(\theta, \phi, x - \Delta)$. Using the bookkeeping technique described in Sec.

11 and 18, and passing to the limit as $\Delta \to 0$, we obtain the rather intimidating nonlinear partial differential-integral equation

$$\frac{1}{\lambda}\left[\frac{\partial R}{\partial x}(v, u, x) + \left(\frac{1}{u} + \frac{1}{v}\right) R(v, u, x)\right]$$

$$= \left[1 + \frac{1}{2}\int_0^1 R(w, u, x)\frac{dw}{w} + \frac{1}{2}\int_0^1 R(v, z, x)\frac{dz}{z}\right] \tag{2}$$

$$+ \frac{1}{4}\left(\int_0^1 R(w, u, x)\frac{dw}{w}\right)\left(\int_0^1 R(v, z, x)\frac{dz}{z}\right).$$

Here $R(v, u, x) = r(\cos\theta, \cos\phi, x)$, with $v = \cos\theta$, $u = \cos\phi$, with the obvious initial condition $r(\theta, \phi, 0) = 0$.

Despite its apparent complexity, this equation is readily susceptible of a computational solution routinely with the aid of a digital computer. Furthermore, only elementary ideas of analysis are required from this stage on. The essence of the ease of solution is that this new formulation results in an *initial value* problem. We are perfectly willing to sacrifice linearity in return for this more convenient analytic structure as far as numerical solution is concerned. This new formulation has distinct analytic advantages as well, but their explanation would take me too far off course.

21. Quadrature Techniques

In order to unleash our digital computer, it is necessary to convert Eq. 20.2 to a finite system of ordinary differential equations. This conversion will naturally be approximate, with the degree of approximation depending upon the size of the system we employ.

To accomplish this conversion, we use the classical technique of numerical quadrature. Given a function $f(x)$ defined over an interval $[a, b]$, we wish to evaluate the integral $I(f) = \int_a^b f(x)\,dx$ in terms of carefully selected values of $f(x)$,

$$\int_a^b f(x)dx \cong \sum_{i=1}^N w_i f(x_i). \tag{1}$$

The question is that of choosing the coefficients, w_i, called the "weights," and the x_i, called the "quadrature points," in some efficient manner. One approach, due to Gauss, is to choose the w_i

and x_i so that (1) is exact for polynomials of degree $2N - 1$ or less. If we take $a = -1$, $b = 1$, we find that the x_i are then the zeroes of the Legendre polynomial of degree N. The w_i, the Christoffel numbers, can also be obtained in terms of the Legendre polynomials.

Before modern computers were available, there was an enormous advantage in using standard approaches, such as that just cited, because the associated values, the x_i and the w_i, were tabulated. With the aid of the computer, we can generate the x_i and w_i from first principles. This means that the more information we have concerning $f(x)$, derived on the basis of physical intuition or from earlier less precise calculations, the more accurate a quadrature formula we can obtain.

All this is connected with the concept of numerical solution as a sequential control process discussed briefly in chapter 1.

With the aid of the foregoing Gaussian quadrature technique, we can replace the Eq. 20.2 by the finite system of nonlinear ordinary differential equations

$$\frac{1}{\lambda}\left[\frac{d}{dx}f_{ij}(x) + \left(\frac{1}{z_i} + \frac{1}{w_j}\right)f_{ij}(x)\right]$$

$$= 1 + \frac{1}{2}\left[\sum_{k=1}^{N}\frac{c_k}{z_k}f_{kj}(x)\right] + \frac{1}{2}\left[\sum_{k=1}^{N}\frac{c_k}{w_k}f_{ik}(x)\right] \qquad (2)$$

$$+ \frac{1}{4}\left[\sum_{k=1}^{N}\frac{c_k}{z_k}f_{kj}(x)\right]\left[\sum_{k=1}^{N}\frac{c_k}{w_k}f_{ik}(x)\right],$$

subject to the initial conditions

$$f_{ij}(0) = 0, \ i, j = 1, 2, \ldots, N. \qquad (3)$$

Here,

$$f_{ij}(x) = R(w_i, z_j, x). \qquad (4)$$

The numerical solution of equations of this type is the one task for which contemporary digital computers are ideally suited. We have N^2 simultaneous equations. They can be reduced to $N(N + 1)/2$ equations if we wish to take advantage of certain symmetries. There is an advantage to keeping the full set as an internal check on the numerical integration.

22. How Large a System?

How large a system of equations of this type can we handle? At Los Alamos in 1944 a method of the kind described was not feasible, because the computer could handle at most ten simultaneous differential equations, which meant that a sufficiently accurate quadratic formula, say $N = 7$ or 9, could not be employed. In 1967 we can think routinely in terms of a thousand such equations. When we write a paper for a journal, we expend a minute or two of computer time to obtain the solution of a hundred simultaneous equations for illustrative purposes.

Within a few years, the solution of ten thousand simultaneous ordinary differential equations subject to initial conditions will be equally routine. Within ten years, we will have the facilities to process a million such equations routinely.

This is not evolution; this is revolution!

23. Reformulation of Mathematical Physics

The ability to obtain the computational solution of large systems of ordinary differential equations means that invariant imbedding can be applied systematically throughout mathematical physics. The fact that the theories of radiative transfer and neutron transport are both based upon a model of particles traversing a medium is not of fundamental significance. What is important is the concept of a "disturbance," a particle, a wave, a shock, or something more complex, entering a medium and interacting with it. The successive interactions constitute a multistage process.

Formulating this process via invariant imbedding, we are led to initial-value problems as opposed to the boundary-value problems of the classical imbedding that lead to Fredholm-type integral equations, or, equivalently, to the problem of solving large systems of linear algebraic equations. This prospect is always unpleasant.

The physicist or engineer can easily absorb the invariant imbedding formulation. Indeed, it is very natural to the experimentalist. With a formulation of this type and with the writing of a foolproof computer program, the best part of the game is over for the mathematician in many fields of mathematical physics. He has discharged his obligations in this domain and can feel free to move on to other, wilder areas of science.

24. Inhomogeneous Media

One difficulty associated with so many of the elegant techniques developed by mathematicians before the advent of the computer is that the techniques depend critically on certain crucial assumptions such as homogeneity, isotropy, and so on. Introduce a realistic atmosphere with anisotropic scattering, and the classically oriented mathematician relapses into a fit of sulking. Add some additional manifestations of the real world, and he leaves the field or, what is worse, remains in the field and ignores the meaningful aspects.

An advantage of the invariant imbedding approach is that homogeneity is of no particular importance. If we take the albedo to be dependent on position, we find that Eq. 20.2 becomes

$$\frac{1}{\lambda(x)}\left[\frac{\partial R}{\partial x}(v, u, x) + \left(\frac{1}{u} + \frac{1}{v}\right) R(v, u, x)\right] = \dots \qquad (1)$$

When we employ quadrature techniques, Eq. 1 is as easy to handle computationally as the case where $\lambda(x)$ is a constant.

25. Anisotropy, Polarization, and Stochastic Media

When the effects of anisotropy and polarization are introduced, systems of equations of the form of Eq. 24.1 are introduced. With the capability of handling large systems of ordinary differential equations afforded by the digital computer, we can employ the simple direct approach just described.

Similarly, we can introduce random effects at the expense of carrying out a large number of calculations of the foregoing nature. This again is no particular obstacle, as parallelization proceeds and computers simultaneously become cheaper and more powerful.

An advantage of the formulation described in Sec. 20 is that it appears to correspond more closely to the actual physical process. A manifestation of this is the fact that the invariant imbedding approach (of which dynamic programming is a specific example) leads to numerically stable equations, whereas the conventional approach leads to unstable ones.

26. Time-dependent Processes

Let us now turn to the problem of time-dependent radiative transfer. The classical imbedding in space and time leads to the equation

$$\mu \frac{\partial I}{\partial x} + \frac{I \partial I}{c \partial t} + \sigma I = \frac{\lambda \sigma}{2} \int_{-1}^{1} I(x, \mu', t) d\mu', \tag{1}$$

subject to various initial and boundary conditions.

Because this equation possesses features even thornier than the steady-state version, it does not seem a promising point of origin as far as a numerical solution is concerned. Let us then turn to an invariant imbedding formulation. If we introduce the function defined as the total reflected flux up to time t as a consequence of incident flux initiating at time 0, we obtain, after some small modifications, an equation of the form

$$g_x + (u^{-1} + v^{-1}) \left(\frac{\partial}{\partial t} + 1 \right) g$$

$$= \lambda \left[\frac{H(t)}{4v} + \frac{1}{2} \int_0^1 g(v, u', x, t) \frac{du'}{u'} + \frac{1}{2v} \int_0^1 g(v', u, x, t) dv' \right. \tag{2}$$

$$\left. + \int_0^t dt' \int_0^1 g(v', u, x, t') dv' \int_0^1 g_t(v, u', x, t - t') \frac{du'}{u'} \right].$$

This equation does not look particularly promising either, taking into account the two partial derivatives, the convolution term, and the nonlinearity. If, however, we introduce the Laplace transform of g, the function $P(v, u, x, s)$ defined by

$$\int_0^\infty g e^{-st} dt = P(v, u, x, s)/4v, \tag{3}$$

we find that P satisfies an equation of familiar form,

$$P_x + (s + 1)(u^{-1} + v^{-1})P = \lambda \left\{ \frac{1}{s} + \frac{1}{2} \int_0^1 P(v, u', x, s) \frac{du'}{u'} \right.$$

$$+ \frac{1}{2} \int_0^1 P(v', u, x, s) \frac{dv'}{v'} \tag{4}$$

$$\left. + \frac{s}{4} \int_0^1 \int_0^1 P(v', u, x, s) P(v, u', x, s) \frac{dv'}{v'} \frac{du'}{u'} \right\},$$

with the initial condition $P(v, u, 0, s) = 0$.

This equation is almost identical with the equation obtained in the time-independent case. Hence, we know that we can obtain the numerical values of $P(v, u, x, s)$ for any $s \geq 0$. But what good does it do us as far as determining the values of $g(v, u, x, t)$ and thus solving the original problem?

27. Numerical Inversion of the Laplace Transform

The success of the foregoing approach to the application of invariant imbedding to time-dependent processes thus hinges upon our ability to obtain a numerical inversion of the Laplace transform. The first difficulty that one faces is that it is impossible! Therefore, prudent people avoid the Laplace transform as a computational tool. But we had no choice, fortunately.

I mean by this statement of impossibility that the operator inverse to the Laplace transform is unbounded or, equivalently, unstable. Given the integral equation

$$L(u) = \int_0^\infty u(t)e^{-st}dt = f(s), \tag{1}$$

it is easy to show that arbitrarily small changes in $f(s)$ can be the consequence of arbitrarily large changes in $u(t)$. That is, no measurements of $f(s)$ to any degree of accuracy can guarantee to produce $u(t)$ to some specified degree of approximation. For example, consider the familiar formula

$$\int_0^\infty e^{-st} \sin at\, dt = \frac{a}{s^2 + a^2}. \tag{2}$$

We observe that

$$\frac{a}{s^2 + a^2} < \frac{a}{a^2} = \frac{1}{a}. \tag{3}$$

Thus, by taking a sufficiently large, we can make $L(\sin at)$ arbitrarily and uniformly small for $s \geq 0$. Nonetheless, $\sin at$ remains of amplitude one.

Thus the unrestricted problem of determining the Laplace inverse has no significance. It does, however, make both mathematical and scientific sense to ask for the Laplace inverse when we know enough about the structure of the desired function $u(t)$ to rule out the presence of high harmonics that produce oscillations such as $\sin at$. Fortunately, in many important scientific problems we know in advance that $u(t)$ is "smooth."

28. Quadrature Techniques

One approach to numerical inversion that has been found successful is to make a change of variable

$$e^{-t} = r \tag{1}$$

which converts the integral Eq. 27.1 to the form

$$\int_0^1 u(\log \frac{1}{r}) r^{s-1} dr = f(s). \tag{2}$$

The use of a quadrature formula of the form described converts Eq. 2 into a linear equation

$$\sum_{i=1}^{N} w_i u \left(\log \frac{1}{r_i} \right) r_i^{s-1} = f(s). \tag{3}$$

Setting $s = 1, 2, \ldots, n$, we obtain a system of linear algebraic equations that can be solved for the N quantities $\{u(\log 1/r_i)\}$. Fortunately, the matrix $(w_i r_i^{j-1})$ can be inverted once and for all with the result that we obtain a relation

$$u \left(\log \frac{1}{r_i} \right) = \sum_{j=1}^{N} a_{ij}^{(N)} f(j), i = 1, 2, \ldots, N, \tag{4}$$

with the $a_{ij}^{(N)}$ tabulated quantities. This explicit solution of Eq. 3 greatly improves the accuracy of the inversion technique, because we no longer have to depend upon an algorithm to solve linear algebraic equations. In this case, this is quite important inasmuch as the matrix $(w_i r_i^{j-1})$ is ill conditioned, as might be expected from the unboundedness of the inverse Laplace transform.

Once a simple representation of this type has been obtained, there is a strong temptation to use Laplace transform techniques in a systematic way to obtain a *computational solution* (as opposed to the standard analytic solutions) of many equations of classic type; that is, equations such as

$$k(x)u_t = u_{xx},$$

$$u(t) = f(t) + \int^t k(t - t_1) u(t_1) dt_1, \tag{5}$$

$$u'(t) = au(t) + bu(t - 1),$$

and even some equations of unexpected type, such as

$$u_t = u_{xx} + u^2,$$
$$u'(t) = u(t - 1) + u(t)^2. \tag{6}$$

At first sight, it may seem surprising that a linear operation such as the Laplace transform can be used to study nonlinear equations. These investigations lead to still other analytic questions, and so on. The point that I wish to highlight without getting too involved in detail is that the constant emphasis upon numerical results, obtained efficiently and simply with the aid of a computer, leads naturally and almost inevitably to new and interesting mathematical ideas and problems.

Efficient numerical inversion techniques will have a considerable effect on the field of numerical solution of partial differential equations.

29. On-Line Control

Also noteworthy is that this roundabout route through mathematical physics provides an approach to a problem that has plagued us in control theory—the problem of determining the future time history of a complex system, say one ruled by a partial differential equation, or a differential-difference equation, in a time short enough to make use of this information.

One advantage of using the Laplace transform technique is that it provides a knowledge of only a few values of $u(t)$; namely, the values $\{u(\log 1/r_i)\}$. The other values can be obtained by interpolation if desired. Because only a few values are computed, the calculation can be done quite quickly. We are thus in a position to carry out effective prediction.

30. Spherical Atmosphere

Sooner or later even the scientist must face the fact that the earth is not flat. One consequence of this fact so adroitly exploited by

Columbus is that atmospheres are spherical in nature rather than of the character of plane-parallel regions. If we apply invariant imbedding to the question of determining the flux reflected from a spherical shell atmosphere surrounding a planet, we obtain a truly formidable equation,

$$\frac{\partial S(z, v, u)}{\partial z} + \frac{1 - v^2}{vz}\frac{\partial S}{\partial v} + \frac{1 - u^2}{uz}\frac{\partial S}{\partial u} + \left(\frac{1}{v} + \frac{1}{u}\right)S - \frac{v^2 + u^2}{v^2 u^2}\frac{S}{z}$$
$$= \lambda \left[1 + \frac{1}{2}\int_0^1 S(z, v, u')\frac{du'}{u'}\right]\left[1 - \frac{1}{2}\int_0^1 S(z, v', u)\frac{dv'}{v'}\right]. \tag{1}$$

Fortunately, the experience gained using standard quadrature methods in connection with plane-parallel atmospheres leads us to try a similar method to eliminate the partial derivatives. Let us write

$$f'(t_i) = \sum_{j=1}^{N} a_{ij}\, f(t_j), i = 1, 2, \ldots, N, \tag{2}$$

where the t_i are the quadrature points used above and determine the coefficients a_{ij} by the condition that the approximation formula be correct for polynomials of degree $N - 1$ or less.

Using this method, and the conventional quadrature already described to eliminate the integral terms, we once again transform the problem into that of solving a large system of ordinary differential equations subject to initial conditions.

31. Identification of Systems

My theme, played over and over, has been the use of the ability to solve large systems of ordinary differential equations subject to initial conditions; and I have embroidered on it in various ways. Considering how successful our assaults upon various citadels of mathematical physics have been, it is impossible to resist the impulse to use the same kind of simple direct approach even more audaciously. Can we begin to consider the really important problems of science, the inverse problems, the identification of systems on the basis of observation and experimentation?

It comes as a bit of a shock when one first realizes that the real problem of science is not so much "What is the answer?" as "What is the question?" In textbooks and in the majority of research papers, we see equations blithely displayed and systematic attempts made to resolve these equations. Yet very seldom is there any discussion of what is to be done with these solutions once they are found. Often arbitrary parameters (cross sections, constants of proportionality, and so on) occur in these equations. It is tacitly assumed by the author, and thus by the student, that these constants are known. In many cases where fields have been thoroughly studied for more than a hundred years, this is so. In many other cases, particularly in the new areas of science, it is not so. As a matter of fact, it is often the solution of the equation that is most easily obtained by direct observation, as in much of astrophysics and neutron transport theory, with the real problem that of determining the parameters.

In some cases the underlying theory is so well established that it is only a matter of obtaining these values. The equations are known to be valid approximations. In still other cases, a number of basic assumptions have been made concerning state variables and the laws of interaction. Hence, the theory will stand or fall on the ability to obtain these parameters and thus the ability to show that there is a reasonable agreement between the predictions of the theory and observation.

We see, then, that mathematical analysis cannot validate any theory, but it can readily invalidate it. This contribution, of course, is enormous; because by discarding all kinds of *a priori* plausible hypotheses, we can come that much closer to more realistic and useful interpretations.

Consider, for example, a question of much interest at present, that of ascertaining the nature of the atmosphere of Venus. At the moment, we have no means for measuring the properties of the atmosphere at different levels above the planet, nor of determining the properties of the planet itself. We do, however, have various measurements concerning the intensity of light that has penetrated the Venusian atmosphere and has been reflected back after various interactions of the type described. Starting with these data, we can make various hypotheses concerning the types of strata that exist, their thickness, and the kinds of scattering, absorption, and radiation interactions that take place within these layers. Using these hypotheses in equations of the kinds displayed in the preceding pages, we can make the calculations and compare the predicted results with the observed results.

Guessing the various parameters involved is risky, and carrying out systematic exploration of parameter ranges is not feasible. Can this search for suitable parameter values be done in a straightforward and efficient manner? The answer is affirmative, granted the kind of arithmetical ability that I have been insisting upon and a certain amount of scientific expertise on the part of the user. We cannot reasonably expect to determine the nature of the interiors of the traditional "black boxes" of physics solely on the basis of external evidence, and we don't expect mathematics to furnish a magic wand. But we can expect to mix some external information, some information about the structure, and sophisticated mathematics to obtain ever more detailed information.

One method of approach to these problems is based on the theory of *quasilinearization*. We have used this successfully in areas ranging from radiative transfer to cardiology.

32. Eclecticism Rampant

I have been presenting the merits of this new approach to mathematical physics in a forceful fashion. I am not merely tilting at windmills nor setting up straw men to demolish. A strong argument is, unfortunately, necessary, because the university is, on the whole, a bastion of conservatism in the intellectual domain. Only someone who has tried to introduce a new mathematical or scientific technique into the academic monastery can fully appreciate how hilarious is the concept of the university as a hotbed of wild-eyed radicalism. Several generations are often required to replace the old courses and the old textbooks; sometimes more.[10]

However, once we have made a dent in the walls of tradition, we must make equally sure that we have not replaced one orthodoxy by another. The history of science, and indeed the history of human culture, shows clearly that the fate of most reform movements is to create another orthodoxy, often far worse than what was supplanted.

The approach of invariant imbedding gives rise to a nonlinear equation subject to initial conditions, and the classical approach provides linear equations subject to boundary-value conditions.

[10] From what I have read, it was sixty-seven years after the death of Newton before his theories were taught at Cambridge and Oxford.

Each approach has advantages. The sensible person in such a situation asks, "Why not use both?"[11]

In certain aspects of the analysis of a process, linearity is an enormous boon and, occasionally, vital to success; in other aspects it may be a serious disadvantage. Consistent with what I have said, scientific philosophy should be a help, not a hindrance. There is no need to vow to use only one mathematical method for the rest of one's life. Nor is it prostitution of one's talents to aid and abet imagination with the ability to do arithmetic.

To illustrate this point, we have found significant ways to reduce the dimensionality of computational problems in radiative transfer by combining certain aspects of invariant imbedding with the properties of a fundamental set of functions introduced by Chandrasekhar into the classical theory.

The idea of the mathematical game that we set out to play so seriously is to furnish the scientist with a tool chest of techniques. Because each method possesses certain advantages and disadvantages, it is up to the user to do some impedance matching, to fit the tool to the problem.[12] This mixing of ideas and compromise between methods is the essence of science—indeed, the essence of culture—and education should be directed toward this goal. Only an unsophisticated person can believe that the complexities of the world can be handled from inside the confines of a narrow orthodoxy. Only a naïve scientist can assume that either singular integral equations or some other single powerful analytic tool or the digital computer alone can resolve all the problems in his area of interest.

An approach with intellectual blinders on is an uneducated approach—certainly uncultured. Unfortunately, this type of approach to major problems is fostered in the undergraduate and graduate schools of the major universities of the country. In opposition to this approach, the truly educated person insists upon examining all aspects of a theory and all theories before committing himself to a course of action.

A valuable consequence of this discussion of two types of imbed-

---

[11] Note the analogy with the comments in chapter 1 concerning the use of dual theories, such as the calculus of variations and dynamic programming applied to control theory.

[12] To paraphrase Gilbert and Sullivan, "Our object all sublime is to fit the computer to the time—available."

ding is that it points up the possibility of many other types. If there are two ways, there must be an unlimited number. This is a useful metaphysical principle.

33. Gradient Techniques

To illustrate the last point, I shall mention briefly the gradient technique. The gradient technique is a method for imbedding an equation of the form

$$T(u) = 0, \tag{1}$$

considered as an equation describing a stationary process, within a family of equations describing a dynamic process,

$$\frac{du}{dt} = T(u). \tag{2}$$

There are many ways of doing this to achieve certain desired objectives. Generally, we use an equation of the form

$$\frac{du}{dt} = G(T(u)), \tag{3}$$

with the property that a solution of $G(T(u)) = 0$ is $T(u) = 0$. The method of successive approximations is a discrete version of the gradient method.

Let me note in passing that the invariant imbedding approach applied to a time-dependent version furnishes a family of equations quite different in form from Eq. 2.

34. Hybrid Computers

So far, I have been emphasizing the digital computer, which means that I wish to emphasize iterative techniques. If I think in terms of an analog computer, then I may want to transform a problem involving iteration, i.e. an initial-value problem, back to a boundary-value problem. Granted the use of the new and more versatile computers that are currently being built—the hybrid computers, part digital, part analog, and part intuition on the part of the user—a new type of mathematical problem arises, that of partitioning the computational solution of a problem into subcomputations. Some of these calculations will be carried out solely by digital techniques; some, by analog techniques; and some, using the resources of the human operator.

New and difficult mathematical problems will arise with this type of computer. I want to stress in particular the concept of numerical solution as an adaptive control process involving a man-machine system.

The key to the solution of the most important problems in science and engineering is to reduce the information pattern or, equivalently, the dimensionality of the system. In some way, we must reduce the amount of data and calculation required to specify the action of a part of the system. An impetus to solving problems of this type comes from studying the basic systems of economics and engineering. There are a multitude of problems of this type in statistical and quantum mechanics and in chemistry. These problems involving large complex systems require entirely new mathematical methods, even with the contemplated computer of the year 2000.

Biology is a field where complexities raise their charming heads in even the simplest models. This situation is true in the mathematical biosciences in general. I shall discuss some reasons for these difficulties in the next chapter, in the course of describing some of the challenges in these new areas of research.

References and Comments

§1. Leibniz commented, "So also the games in themselves merit to be studied and if some penetrating mathematician meditated upon them he would find many important results, for man has never shown more ingenuity than in his plays."—From:
Ore, O. 1960. Pascal and the invention of probability theory. *Amer. Math. Monthly,* 67: 409–16.

§2. See the article:
Wigner, E. 1960. The unreasonable effectiveness of mathematics in the natural sciences. *Comm. Pure Appl. Math.,* 13: 1–14.

§7. The development of the theory of invariant imbedding was started together with Robert Kalaba in 1956. The first paper was in 1956:
Bellman, R., and R. Kalaba. 1956. On the principle of invariant imbedding and propagation through inhomogeneous media. *Proc. Nat. Acad. Sci.,* 42: 629–32.
Subsequently, a great deal of joint work was done with G. M. Wing, S. Ueno, R. Vasudevan, and H. Kagiwada. See, for example:

Bellman, R., R. Kalaba, and S. Ueno. 1963. On the diffuse reflection of parallel rays by an inhomogeneous flat layer as a limiting process. *J. Math. Anal. and Appl.*, 7: 91–99.

Bellman, R., R. Kalaba, and R. Vasudevan. 1963. Invariant imbedding and the Townsend avalanche. *J. Math. Anal. and Appl.*, 7: 264–70.

Bellman, R., R. Kalaba, and G. M. Wing. 1960. Invariant imbedding and mathematical physics—I: Particle processes. *J. Math. Phys.*, 1: 280–308.

Bellman, R., and others. Computational solution of radiative transfer problems in cloud physics. *Conference on Cloud Physics Proceedings* (to appear).

See also:

Redheffer, R. 1954. Novel uses of functional equations. *J. Rat. Mech. Anal.*, 3: 271–79.

———. 1960. The Myciolski-Pazkowski diffusion problem. *J. Rat. Mech. Anal.*, 9: 607–21.

———. 1961. Difference and functional equations and transmission line theory. *Modern Mathematics for the Engineer*, Series II. E. F. Beckenbach, editor. McGraw-Hill Book Company, New York. Pp. 282–337.

For detailed accounts of the application of invariant imbedding to neutron transport theory and radiative transfer, see the books:

Bellman, R., R. Kalaba, and M. Prestrud. 1963. *Invariant Imbedding and Radiative Transfer in Slabs of Finite Thickness.* American Elsevier Publishing Company, New York.

Bellman, R., and others. 1964. *Invariant Imbedding and Time-dependent Transport Processes.* American Elsevier Publishing Company, New York.

Wing, G. M. 1962. *An Introduction to Transport Theory.* John Wiley & Sons, New York.

§11. The book is:
Chandrasekhar, S. 1950. *Radiative Transfer.* Oxford University Press, London.

§13. See, for example:
Bellman, R., R. Kalaba, and G. M. Wing. 1960. Invariant imbedding and the reduction of two-point boundary-value problems to initial-value problems. *Proc. Nat. Acad. Sci.*, 46: 1646–49.

§15. See:
Ambarzumian, V. A. 1943. Diffuse reflection of light by a foggy medium. *Compt. Rend. Acad. Sci. URSS*, 38: 229–32.

Ambarzumian, V. A., and others. 1952. *Teoreticheskaya Astrofizika.* Moscow.

§21. For a detailed discussion of quadrature techniques, see the book:
Bellman, R., R. Kalaba, and J. Lockett. 1966. *Numerical Inversion of*

the Laplace Transform. American Elsevier Publishing Company, New York.

§23. For a discussion of applications of invariant imbedding to various parts of mathematical physics, see the paper by Bellman, Kalaba, and Wing cited in §7 and:

Adams, R., and E. Denman. 1966. *Wave Propagation and Turbulent Media.* American Elsevier Publishing Company, New York.

Bellman, R., and R. Kalaba. 1967. New methods for the solution of partial differential equations. *Proc. Delaware Symposium.* Academic Press, Inc., New York.

Bellman, R., H. Kagiwada, and R. Kalaba. 1965. Invariant imbedding and nonvariational principles in analytical dynamics. *Internat. J. Nonlinear Mechanics,* 1: 51–55.

§27. Numerous applications of the Laplace transform will be found in the book cited in §21.

§30. See:

Bellman, R., H. Kagiwada, and R. Kalaba. 1966. Invariant imbedding and radiative transfer in spherical shells. *J. Computer Physics,* 1: 245–56.

Bellman, R. 1968. Invariant imbedding and computational methods in radiative transfer. *Proc. Symposia in Applied Mathematics,* Vol. XIX. Amer. Math. Soc., Providence, Rhode Island.

§31. See:

Bellman, R., and R. Kalaba. 1965. *Quasilinearization and Nonlinear Boundary Value Problems.* American Elsevier Publishing Company, New York.

Bellman, R., and R. Roth. 1966. Segmental differential approximation and biological systems: An analysis of a metabolic process. *J. Theoret. Biol.,* 11: 168–76.

Bellman, R., B. Gluss, and R. Roth. 1965. Segmental differential approximation and the "black box" problem. *J. Math. Anal. and Appl.,* 12: 91–104.

three

THE CHALLENGE OF

THE MATHEMATICAL

BIOSCIENCES

1. Introduction

Perhaps what a mathematician does in the area of the biosciences requires some explanation. After all, many of you will recall that even as recently as ten years ago, a mathematician was something of a novelty in a department of engineering. Nowadays it is taken for granted that there are advantages to engineering in having the services of these practitioners of the black arts. Furthermore, it is gradually becoming apparent that there is a great deal to be gained for mathematics itself in the investigation of problems arising in the engineering domain. The same situation holds in the biosciences, as I hope to show.

Occasionally, when asked what mathematicians are doing in biosciences, I rely with a paraphrase of a famous comment, "Medicine is too important to be left completely to doctors." I must add, however, that it is also too important to be left to mathematicians. No mathematician armed with a computer and tables of statistics can take the place of the doctor. Previously, it was necessary to reassure the patient; now it is necessary to reassure the doctor that he is absolutely essential and cannot possibly be replaced by any combination of technological devices.

At any rate, one purpose of the mathematician in these complex areas, as in the domains of engineering, physics, and economics, is to assist the specialist in his work; to perform for him a number of auxiliary tasks of purely mathematical nature; and thus to make it easier, and indeed feasible, to carry out his principal functions. I have stressed this point in the preceding chapters in connection with the scientist. As in the other domains mentioned, the mathematician in the biosciences will be richly rewarded for his apparent altruism. In any case, as a human being who presumably will need medical care himself, there is an immediate return.

Perhaps a good way to present some idea of what a mathematician can contribute in the biosciences is to present brief sketches of some activities in which I have been personally engaged. It is certainly the easiest and most interesting way as far as I am concerned. I will start with some problems that are easily stated and then slowly ascend the scale of apparent mathematical complication. The surprising point, as usual, is that the really complicated problems are easy to state and that many of the questions that seem most complex are most amenable to mathematical techniques.

The mathematician becomes reconciled over time to the fact that the most difficult challenges he faces can be stated in a few words, all completely understandable to any school child. As a matter of fact, one reason that it has been so hard to get scientifically well-trained people interested in some problem areas described later has been lack of comprehension by the amateur or novice of the true intellectual levels of the problems. Once a problem area becomes intellectually respectable, with the seal of approval of the universities, then research workers flock into it. The difficulty at that point, for the individual researcher, is that he is then competing against hundreds and thousands of others and often doing work of marginal value. On the other hand, one advantage of pioneering is the privilege of roaming at will over a vast domain, picking and choosing problems of great personal interest.

2. Data Storage and Retrieval

One of the basic scientific problems in this country today, far more difficult than any of those connected with space travel or with high-energy physics and certainly far more vital to the feasible operation of our society, is the efficient storage and retrieval of data. In other words, we want to develop techniques for efficient conversion of data to information.

The question does not seem very profound. What could possibly be difficult about storing several hundred, or several thousand records, or, as computers become more powerful, several million records?

To make the question more specific, suppose we make it task oriented. How can we improve the operation of the general practitioner, or specialist, either in his office or in the clinic? One answer is obvious: we could provide more information concerning the patient more quickly, and in a way that can be easily absorbed.

Consider, for example, some of the questions associated with a big city hospital, say the Los Angeles County General Hospital, which is the biggest in the country. If a patient has been using the services of the hospital for some time, as both an in-patient and an out-patient, an enormous store of data has been gathered about his present and past condition. These data are displayed on various charts, in the handwriting of the different attending physicians, and often in the abbreviated forms that are perfectly intelligible to anyone in the specialty. With this in mind, think of this patient's next visit to the clinic, waiting to see a doctor who may have twenty, thirty, or more patients waiting to see him.

If the doctor is personally familiar with the patient, he has a certain head start in knowing what to look for. If not, he has to skim through a mass of material in a few minutes, attempting to correlate with past history information gained from the patient himself. What should he look for? What facts should be displayed for his immediate attention? How should they be displayed?

These questions are on a very simple conceptual level. Only when one looks into the details of storing and retrieving hundreds of millions, and billions, of pieces of data in various ways for different kinds of users does one realize the complexity of the problem.

Another point should be made. Intuitively, we all feel that data is valuable. Yet we all remember the point of "The Purloined Letter." Vital facts in plain view can easily be masked by masses of other extraneous facts. What point is there to giving the attending physician a telephone book of statistics concerning a patient if he has only a small amount of time to go through it and does not know where to look first? How can the research doctor get the basic information he needs from years and years of hospital records stored in basements? Ironically, in many states hospitals are forced to keep this data for a specified number of years. Yet it is almost completely useless in its current form because we possess neither the manpower nor the means for digesting it. Only when it is computerized will it serve its intended purposes.

Perhaps the easiest way to sum up the preceding discussion is the comment, *data is not information*. Information is data that we want to use for decisionmaking. We desperately need a set of filtering techniques for reducing masses of data to the essence required at the moment. Observe that we are back to "on-line control." Time is of the essence.

3. Averting Tragedies

The following sad tale illustrates the urgency of having vital information available. About a year ago, a little girl was brought to a big city hospital by her devoted grandmother. The child's parents had gone away on a well-deserved weekend rest and had left the child with the grandmother. About one o'clock on Saturday morning, the child woke up complaining of fever, sore throat, headache, and pains. The very conscientious grandmother got dressed and took the child to the Emergency Clinic. An intern on duty, observing the symptoms cited, gave the child an injection of an antibiotic and sent her home.

Unfortunately, unknown to him, the child was a victim of nephritis, a kidney ailment. She had been kept alive in reasonably good health for the last two years by a team of doctors who had monitored her behavior very carefully, day by day. In particular, antibiotics were absolutely forbidden. By Saturday noon, the child was dead.

With the simplest type of bookkeeping system, using very rudimentary business machines, the warning, "NO ANTIBIOTICS," would have been made instantly available to the intern. Typing the name and identifying number of the child into a computer system would have resulted in an immediate reply on a priority basis. The overall problem of retrieval is certainly difficult, but it is easy to provide this kind of emergency information.

4. Drug Reactions

Situations like this one occur repeatedly. The general public is, fortunately for their sense of well-being, unacquainted with the magnitude of both the drug reaction and the drug administration problems; indeed, many physicians are themselves not sufficiently aware of the dangers.

To obtain some idea of the importance of this fundamental area, medical research groups have sent teams to hospitals to follow physicians on their rounds. They have compared their observation of drug reactions in patients with those noted by the physician. Conservatively, there seem to be five to ten times as many serious effects as are usually reported by the physician unaware of the many manifestations of side effects. Add this fact to the results of other studies that show how often either the wrong drug is administered or the right drug is given in the wrong dosage, and one begins to have an idea of the magnitude of the problem of drug prescription. This information is strong motivation for the introduction of systematic techniques in this area based on computer systems combined with high-powered statistical techniques and methods of operations research.

I am sure that you are all familiar with the thalidomide tragedy that has resulted in about thirty thousand children being born in Europe with major deformities—no arms, no forearms, and so forth. I shall mention this tragedy again later in connection with prosthetics and orthotics. A corresponding situation in this country, which could have produced several hundred thousand critically crippled children, was barely averted by the intelligence, and what can only be described as "guts," of one woman, Frances O. Kelsey. An avid reader of all kinds of medical research journals, her attention was caught by an item pointing out the possible harmful consequences of thalidomide. By sheer force of will she held up the distribution of thalidomide in this country by major drug companies.

With even a rudimentary computerized system for the dissemination of experimental results indicating serious possible side effects, this information would have been widely available throughout the world, a routine application of the storage and retrieval of information. It is a pity that systems of this type were not installed at least ten years ago, and it is certainly hard to estimate the cost to the American public in suffering because of the lack of such a system. But, to paraphrase another well-known aphorism, "People get the kind of science they deserve." It is still difficult to convince the American people that there are important areas of science other than "man in space" at five or ten billion dollars a year and "atom smashers" at half a billion dollars apiece. Ironically, the scientific community is almost totally united against these perversions of the intellectual spirit.

5. Memory

I have been emphasizing the feasibility of computerized systems that could provide warning signals. The overall problem of designing a computerized system for the extensive storage and retrieval of medical data is another, and far more intricate, matter. Essentially, we are entering the area of artificial intelligence and thus are being forced reluctantly to examine the nature of memory, recognition of facts, and so forth. Because we have absolutely no information at the present time as to how the human brain carries out its remarkable feats of memory, recognition, and learning, we cannot merely follow well-established techniques in designing computer systems to accomplish the same tasks.

We are forced to improvise, with the result that we currently employ extremely primitive methods for storage of data. Problems of this nature are formidably difficult precisely because they have no complexity. Complexity is a consequence of structure. Once the structure is understood, we can turn the complexity to our own ends. But what do we do with the total data concerning a million patients a year at a hospital? How do we organize and group the information concerning a patient so that each of a half a dozen specialists, ranging from an orthopedic surgeon to a neurosurgeon, can obtain the information he needs in a reasonable time? How do we make sure that the information bank is constantly updated? How do we use some of the available data for research purposes, ranging from the study of kidney disease in expectant mothers to the effects of digitalis on senior citizens?

Once again, let me emphasize that the questions are easy to pose but the answers unknown. No one has any good ideas at the present. These are particular aspects of the new theory of large systems.

Consequently, it is important to realize, when you read Sunday supplement articles about the computerization of hospitals, that there is a great deal more to it than just pouring in men, money, and computers. These are certainly essential, but a major research effort will be required to make these techniques truly effective and operational. One might think, in view of the Medicare program and the avalanche of paper work that is threatening to impede the proper functioning of hospitals, that a crash program of this nature would be initiated. Whether it does or does not depends on the American public.

6. Community Service

As the citizens of this country begin to take seriously their responsibilities to each other, we encounter not only increasing problems of storage and retrieval of information, but also questions of the scheduling of activities. Inside a hospital, there are the problems of arranging for data taking, for X rays, for blood tests, for operations, for the washing of laundry, and for preparing special diets. In other words, the hospital has its "hotel" aspects, as they are called, as well as the direct medical aspects.

But the hospital, in turn, is only one of a number of community services. As we examine the many problems of the community, ranging from the testing and teaching of deaf and partially deaf children to the care and supervision of incapacitated elderly people, we begin to realize that there are major tasks involved in coordinating a variety of services for the citizens, in using effectively the resources we have, and in introducing new kinds of services.

These major undertakings are slowly getting off the ground. Unhappily, only lately has it been "fashionable" to study these problems. It is important to prepare welfare programs carefully and to carry them out well, not only for the obvious reasons, but also because there are still powerful segments of our society resolutely opposed to community services. These groups are eager to use every failure as an excuse to sabotage the entire concept.

7. Medical Diagnosis

Let us suppose that we have overcome a number of obstacles and have introduced an efficient system for making available the pertinent data to the physician. Can we do anything further to help him make use of it? In other words, is there any way in which mathematical techniques can assist in medical diagnosis? This is a problem in the identification of systems, as I shall emphasize later.

One way to view medical diagnosis is as a problem of establishing a one-to-one correspondence between the set of observed symptoms and the illnesses and disabilities that are present. One can reasonably expect a physician to be able to do this for the more common ailments, but it is not sensible to expect him to be a "medical encyclopedia," any more than we expect an engineer to be an "engineering handbook." Even the medical schools are beginning to modify their ritual hazing courses in anatomy and physiology in favor of more sophisticated training.

One way that a mathematician with a computer can assist the physician is with rudimentary statistics. Based on hundreds of thousands of case histories, aided by constant updating of data, we can assert that when a certain complex of symptoms is exhibited, then the probability is such and such that disease of type one is the primary cause, such and such that disease of type two is the cause, and so forth. The task is not that simple, of course, because human beings show a large variability in their reactions to different illnesses. Furthermore, there is always the possibility that several illnesses are present at the same time to varying degrees.

Still, the idea of differential diagnosis by computer is alluring. You may ask, "Why not set up a dictionary of symptoms and illnesses? List all sets of symptoms and all sets of diseases, and let the computer do the matching."

The answer to this modest proposal is simple. The complexity of possible behaviors and misbehaviors of the human body is incredible. Consider, for example, the problem of diagnosing heart disease by computer.

I remember talking to a friend at the University of Washington, a cardiologist who saw the possibilities of computers ten years ago, well before the bands started playing. He showed me a matrix that was approximately five hundred by one thousand—five hundred different causes and one thousand different symptoms. Furthermore, he assured me that this matrix was not exhaustive, inasmuch as it pertained only to diseases of the heart. Some elementary calculations will give you some idea of the number of possible combinations of symptoms and ailments. Since the number is extraordinarily large, if we did decide to list them all, there would be the usual problem of storage and retrieval.

Consequently, when you read glowing accounts of computer diagnosis of heart disease, or of other ailments, you can be reasonably sure that a certain amount of preliminary screening has gone on and that this preliminary filtering was done by an expert in the field.

Perhaps the proper analogy is the following. Suppose that you chose a high school team and challenge the top professional football team. It doesn't seem like much of a match. But suppose you decline to name the city where the game is to be held, or the day or time when the game is to be played. Clearly, the pro team is going to have a difficult time winning that game because it cannot guarantee being in the proper spot at game time. This is to a great extent what the problem of diagnosis is. Focus upon a particular area, and reasonably effective statistical techniques can be applied. The major task of the diagnostician is to locate that area.

The principal difficulty in automating this effort is to take conscious account, absolutely required for a computer, of very subtle clues that some human beings can recognize almost intuitively after much experience. The human diagnostician can function brilliantly in this fashion without being able to tell anyone how he does it.

Another of my friends is a well-known neurosurgeon, to some extent the neurosurgeon's neurosurgeon. He is often called in when lesser surgeons have botched matters or have been unable to pinpoint the cause of the patient's continuing distress. One day he was asked to attend a grocer who had been struck on the head during a holdup and was comatose. Since there was a possibility of the need for an immediate surgical procedure due to internal hemorrhage, he ordered that the grocer be taken to the hospital by ambulance immediately. By chance, the surgeon entered the elevator going up to the operating room at the same time that the patient was wheeled in. While the elevator ascended six floors, he examined the patient closely. As the door opened leading to the surgical amphitheatres, he announced that no operation was necessary, that the bleeding would stop by itself in twenty-four hours, and that the patient would recover completely.

Twice during the next two days he looked in on the patient to confirm his diagnosis. With the patient safely recovered and home, he submitted a bill for five hundred dollars. The family was indignant at the thought of paying a sum like this without even an operation, despite the fact that an operation could easily have resulted in the patient's death. They asked for a detailed breakdown of the bill. The breakdown read as follows:

2 hospital visits @ $10.00	$ 20.00
Diagnosis in elevator	480.00
Total	$500.00

He received $200.00 from a grateful family.

The point of this anecdote is that experts can recognize patterns that the ordinary trained person cannot. When I asked this surgeon how he was able to analyze the situation so quickly, he mentioned this feature and that feature, but none of it sounded very convincing. There was no doubt that he knew how to do it, but there seemed to be equally little doubt that he could not communicate the methods that he used. Sherlock Holmes may comment, "You know my methods, Watson," but we also know that Watson never did very well with those methods.

This is the basic problem of artificial intelligence. We have no understanding of how human memory functions, nor of the methods employed by the brain to make decisions in complex situations involving considerable degrees of uncertainty. It is intriguing, and a little frightening, that we know so little about "inner space."

8. Sequential Diagnosis

Nonetheless, there are available some simple ideas that can be fruitfully applied in a number of situations. One idea is a wide-ranging extension of the game of Twenty Questions. Basically, it is an application of the theory of dynamic programming. Instead of attempting to recognize the underlying illness on the basis of the entire set of symptoms at one throw, let us convert the diagnostic process into a multistage decision process.

We begin by asking a particular question. "Is Symptom I present?" If the patient replies that it is, we ask another question pertaining to Symptom Ia. If the answer is negative, we ask a question pertaining to Symptom Ib, and so on. If the questions are chosen carefully, each negative answer rules out a large number of

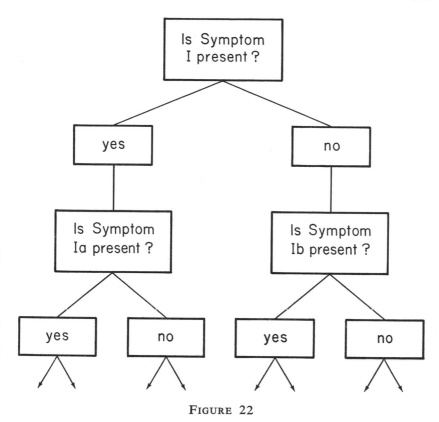

FIGURE 22

possible illnesses. A flow chart for this process is given in Figure 22. The reader familiar with computers will observe that this type of systematic investigation is ideally suited to computer processing.

By using a questioning process of adaptive type, we can eliminate a large number of unnecessary questions and zero in on the desired information very rapidly.

The mathematical problem, familiar to statisticians, is to do this experimentation and testing in some efficient manner. A trained diagnostician learns how to do this. The mathematician, however, finds it difficult to program a computer for this task using only conventional logical and mathematical techniques. The overlapping nature of so many symptom complexes makes the foregoing approach hard to carry out in general. Nevertheless, it is being used successfully in a number of clinics in connection with preliminary screening.

9. Cancer of the Cervix

Let us go on to another possible application of the computer, one that would be of inestimable value if it could be carried through. We begin with the observation that many medical conditions can be readily alleviated if recognized early enough. The problem is to recognize them before the condition is obvious—and untreatable. In other words, we need "early warning" systems for medical treatment. A good example of such a condition is cancer of the cervix, an ailment that afflicts women with steadily increasing frequency from the age of thirty-five or so.

This kind of cancer can be spotted by the gynecologist with very high probability in its earliest stages and, once noticed, can be cured with one hundred percent success. The incidence of the disease is not great, which means that the majority of women examined will exhibit a negative response. It follows that, in some sense, the greater part of this "preventive maintenance" will be wasted. How, then, does one plan a systematic testing program for the population of women over thirty-five in this country?

Clearly, such programs for this and other diseases could tie up all the trained pathologists of the country and effectively prevent them from attending to other duties. Considering the routine nature of the testing and its repetitive nature, it is natural to think of the application of computer techniques.

What is involved in examination for cancer of the cervix? A tissue smear is examined through the microscope or with the aid of a blown-up photograph. An expert looks at the various cell configurations and makes a judgment. Cancer is either present or not present.

The problem, then, is one of pattern recognition. Presumably, we should be able to computerize this task in a straightforward fashion. The sensible approach is to take several hundred thousand tissue smears, some cancerous and some not, and use a group of experts to provide a consensus concerning the features that impel them to a decision one way or the other. Unfortunately, this situation is similar to the one described in connection with the neurosurgeon. The pathologist can recognize the condition when it arises, but he cannot tell in complete detail in advance how he goes about the decision process. Several groups at IBM and other research installations have worked on this problem for years, but so far the results apparently have been nil.

10. Pattern Recognition

Some tasks in pattern recognition are simple. For example, there is little difficulty in designing machines that will read addresses for the Post Office, provided that all of these addresses are typed in a standard format. Allow all, or even some, of the varieties of human handwriting that exist, and the problem becomes formidable. Techniques can be devised for all-purpose reading of handwriting, but they are too unreliable to use at present. Possibly, the effective systems of the future will use a man-machine combination. Now, the simplest technique might be to use a reward system—to offer lower rates and faster service for those companies and individuals who use standard addressing methods and cooperate in other ways. This is a trend at the moment.

The interesting fact that comes through as soon as these processes of pattern recognition are analyzed is that we can perform all sorts of intricate operations that we don't really understand. In actuality, we observe the opposite of the standard dictum of the high school teacher, "If you really understand it, you can explain it in words."

It seems that there are no human actions of any subtlety, elegance, or importance that we totally comprehend. There is no way to tell someone how to develop a good backhand in tennis, how to play chess, how to compose music, how to do research, etc., etc., etc. We can demonstrate some of the simpler aspects of the entire process, we can provide good and bad examples, and we can correct some obvious faults; but we cannot dissect the activity in a step-by-step fashion. This is the principal reason why the computer is limited in its abilities at present. Furthermore, it is not clear that the situation will ever significantly improve. Any detailed defense of this statement would get me enmeshed in chapter 1 again, and a cyclic lecture series is too much to endure.

11. Intelligent Machines

A fundamental contribution to these areas that can be made by the mathematician is a careful analysis of what is involved in the recognition of patterns, in the learning of abilities, in the programming of computers, and so on. A first step is the construction of various classes of processes and of hierarchies of processes. As in the scientific world, once we have some kind of classification scheme, we have a useful way of matching a method to a problem.

At present, a great deal of effort is devoted to the problem of teaching computers to learn how to perform a task such as pattern recognition. Initially, we are concerned with teaching the computer to perform tasks that we ourselves can perform. A second and more intriguing stage is to program the computer to learn to recognize patterns that we ourselves cannot recognize explicitly.

Toward this aim, we require a sophisticated approach that uses principles that enable the computer first to construct its own language and nomenclature on the basis of sample specimens and then to develop its own discrimination techniques. Many of the classification schemes in fields ranging from weather prediction to geological surveying have evolved like Topsy. They are certainly not based on any intrinsic logical scheme. Consequently, it is possible that new classification methods could develop more effective techniques for computer identification of tissue smears. It is all possible, but it is a long time off at the present time—unless someone comes up with some really bright ideas.

In any case, I want to indicate how the pressures of the biomedical world thrust certain new kinds of mathematical problems upon us. The manpower requirements for the successful operation of the Medicare program of the present, much less the future, force us to look with urgency for the introduction of automatic scanning devices for X rays, cardiograms, blood tests, and so forth. But the mathematical obstacles are considerable.

12. Analysis of Cardiograms

For example, let us examine the problem of using mathematics and computers to analyze cardiograms. Over time, the cardiologist has come to recognize that there are strong connections between various combinations of symptoms and certain ailments. The correspondence is easiest to make when the symptoms are clearest. The trouble with this "wait-and-see" approach is that the clearest symptoms are frequently associated with untreatable cases. Hence, what is urgently required is an early warning system. We want to be able to detect a malfunction as soon as possible so that a number of preventive, or curative, measures can be used.

One approach involves the use of statistical techniques. These techniques are powerful and will remain a basic tool in biomedical research. Frequently, however, important symptoms can be masked by a variety of other "noisy" data, extraneous to the question at hand. In these cases, all-purpose statistical methods are not sufficiently powerful to provide the required discrimination.

Generally, it can be said that the use of statistics is an admission of defeat by the scientist. It means that we understand so little about the underlying mechanism that we are forced to use chance mechanisms and averaging techniques. Sometimes, of course, even with detailed understanding, it is more efficacious and elegant to employ stochastic models. But we should make a conscious choice.

Averaging is a useful technique in statistical mechanics and quantum mechanics, where one rarely cares what happens to an individual atom or electron. But an individual patient is another matter. He prefers not to be regarded as a statistic. He should be, and can be, analyzed and treated as a complex system subject to definite biochemophysical laws.

The electrocardiogram is a step in this direction. A picture of a normal heart may look like Figure 23, but a picture of an abnormal heart may look like Figure 24.

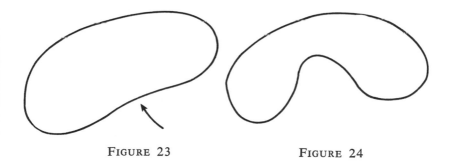

FIGURE 23   FIGURE 24

It doesn't require much training in the interpretation of these phase diagrams to realize that the second picture has serious connotations. But what about the first picture? Observe the indentation singled out by the arrow. Is this a "normal" variation in a healthy individual or an indication of the possible onset of a critical defect in heart function? With the aid of only statistical techniques it is difficult to decide. But "wait and see" attitudes may be costly.

We want to use our detailed information concerning the electro-mechanical structure of the heart to obtain more sensitive discriminators than those furnished by conventional statistical techniques.

13. The Identification of Systems

To illustrate the techniques that can be applied to the study of these questions, consider the simpler problem of determining the structure of an RLC-circuit on the basis of observations over time. That is to say, using measurements of the current at various times, we wish to determine the values of the circuit elements, *R, L,* and *C* (Figure 25).

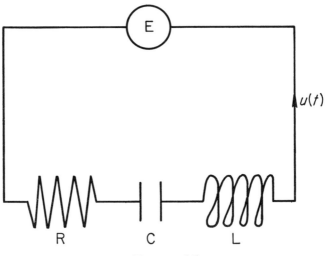

FIGURE 25

Let $u(t)$ represent the current in the circuit at time t so that the equation for $u(t)$ is

$$L\frac{du}{dt} + Ru + \frac{1}{C}\int_0^t udt_1 = E\cos \omega t. \tag{1}$$

In some cases we may wish merely to study the overall behavior of the current as a function of time. In these circumstances, we can look at a picture such as Figure 26. This diagram may represent a satisfactory damping out of the current. Or the picture may be like Figure 27. This diagram may represent a satisfactory, or unsatisfac-

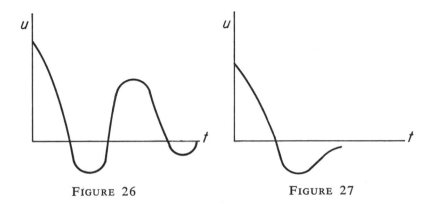

FIGURE 26 FIGURE 27

tory, overdamped system and also indicate that $\omega = 0$, either a desirable or undesirable situation. In any case, a glance tells us what we want to know.

Suppose, however, that there is a certain amount of "noise" due to outside effects, and suppose further that we don't have time to observe the system to see which of the foregoing behaviors is the actual situation. Suppose that we have data over some brief initial time-interval (Figure 28), a set of measurements, $[u(t_i)]$,

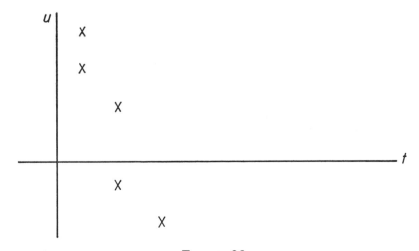

FIGURE 28

$i = 1, 2, \ldots, M$. How do we determine the values of R, L, and C, the driving voltage E_0, the frequency ω, and the initial state of the system? Alternatively, how do we *identify* the system on the basis of observations? Identification here is necessary for prediction of subsequent behavior.

Problems of this nature are fundamental in all areas of the physical and social sciences. It cannot be said that we possess any guaranteed method of resolving them. But with the aid of the mathematician and the computer, we can approach them nowadays in a more systematic fashion, given a sufficient amount of experience and intuition on the part of the scientist.

One approach is the following. Let $b_i = u(t_i)$ denote the measured values of the current and form the expression

$$\sum_{i=1}^{M} [u(t_i) - b_i]^2, \tag{2}$$

where $u(t)$ now represents the solution of Eq. 1. This quantity in Eq. 2 is to be minimized over the missing structural parameters.

This can be done by a direct search technique, essentially "tuning," using an analog computer. As we know, we can train human beings to perform this operation with remarkable speed and accuracy in many cases. In general, however, it is not easy to construct a suitable analog circuit. Consequently we wish to use other, more versatile methods.

Quasilinearization provides a method for questions of this nature, provided we possess some initial estimates of the missing values. As emphasized previously, the mathematician cannot work magic. He needs a substantial scientific base from which to operate, which means close cooperation with the biomedical researcher.

Let me note in passing that as far as the mathematician is concerned, the problem of identification on the basis of observed behavior is equivalent to the problem of designing a system with a certain desired behavior. Thus, we now possess systematic approaches to the optimal design of systems.

14. Cardiology

As mentioned, the diagnosis of heart ailments is a vastly complicated problem. The many real difficulties must not be underestimated. We can, however, make a start on the use of discrimination techniques more powerful than those of statistics using the foregoing methods. We may think of the heart as a set of interconnected RLC circuits as shown in Figure 29.[1]

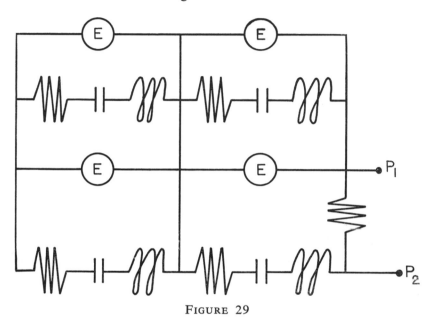

FIGURE 29

If all the circuits are operating properly in phase, we see a voltage of one type across the terminals P_1, P_2. If the individual circuits do not synchronize, or if defects are present in the components, a different time history appears. With the ability to analyze large systems made possible by the computer, we can interpret the nature of the system in terms of easily available measurements.

This point is very important. The possibility of considering the system in entirety means that we can use the results of easily accessible, inexpensive, and reproducible measurements to ascertain the behavior of inaccessible and delicate components. This is a particularly significant new aspect of medical diagnosis opened up by modern mathematics and the computer. The computer is thus as essential to biology as the microscope, and as essential to astronomy as the telescope.

[1] The situation is much more complex, but this is not important as far as the illustration of the basic ideas is concerned.

There are problems similar to the foregoing in the utilization of heart sounds, and many interesting questions arise in connection with the display of this information for the use of the physician.

15. Chemotherapy

Let us now turn to another area of modern medicine where success depends to a considerable extent upon the ability to perform a great deal of arithmetic rapidly. Consider the field of chemotherapy, the cure of diseases by means of chemicals.

A great step in chemotherapy was made by Ehrlich when he discovered his famous 606 as a treatment for syphillis. Nowadays, few biochemists would have the temerity to initiate a program of this type. The number of chemicals currently available for testing is so astronomical that a single individual would feel defeated before he began.

An organization like the Sloan-Kettering Institute for Cancer Research has screened probably millions of candidates for cancer treatment over the years. In view of the magnitude of the task of obtaining efficient drugs, the question arises whether there is any way of using mathematical techniques to provide various kinds of filtering that could reduce the amount of laboratory testing, which is time-consuming, difficult, and expensive—an unpleasant troika.

Clearly, the situation calls for the use of mathematical models. There were two significant obstacles to progress along this road in the past. In the first place, not enough was understood about the basic physiological mechanisms to provide the foundations for a sufficiently sophisticated mathematical model. Second, once constructed, the equations were so unbearably complicated even under the simplest assumptions that nothing could be done with them. They were too involved to solve analytically, and far too large and complicated to solve numerically. Furthermore, many of the basic parameters were unavailable.

The tremendous advances made over the last twenty years in experimental techniques and devices for obtaining measurements, combined with the development of the digital computer, make it reasonable now to consider the construction of realistic mathematical models in many areas of physiology.

Just as in the physical and engineering spheres where we can replace wind tunnels and towing tanks with mathematical models when we gain sufficient understanding, so we can hope to accelerate some of the experimental efforts in the biomedical field. We hope to carry out certain types of experimentation more quickly, more accurately, and far more cheaply with the aid of mathematical models and computers than with laboratory equipment. One reason is that the testing can be done in electronic time rather than in real time. This is our long-term goal, and we do not pretend that we are significantly near it in many areas. But here and there, in carefully chosen cases, we can point to an impressive advance.[2]

In the area of chemotherapy, we can begin with the question, "What kinds of chemicals can we inject into the body that will provide a concentration in one region sufficient to be effective[3] without producing an undue concentration of the chemical, or its off-shoots, someplace else?" (We are back to the drug reaction problem!)

The localization of the action of a drug is perhaps the major problem in chemotherapy. There is little difficulty in finding chemicals that will rapidly destroy tumors and cancers. Unhappily, the great majority of these chemicals will do extensive damage in many other parts of the body. The question is one of focusing.

How would we go about constructing a model of this type? We can begin in a modest fashion, dividing the body into a set of organs and a pumping and mixing mechanism, the heart. We use two sets to illustrate (Figure 30). Needless to add, few of us possess physiological systems as neatly arranged as this one, and a considerable amount of preliminary effort and experience is required even to construct a simple model of this type.

We begin with an injection of a chemical into the bloodstream. The blood flows through the two organs, I and II, resulting in various interactions, and is then mixed in the heart. This process repeats itself every minute or so. When the blood containing the drug passes through an organ, there occur interactions between this

---

[2] One should not be discouraged by the difficulties in biomathematics and bioengineering. Consider the problems encountered in the use of mathematics in treating far simpler systems such as bridges, houses, airplanes, and ships with several hundred years of experience in order to gain the proper perspective.

[3] Observe that we carefully skirt the question of what is meant by effective. There are major research problems in this area whose portrayal would take us too far afield.

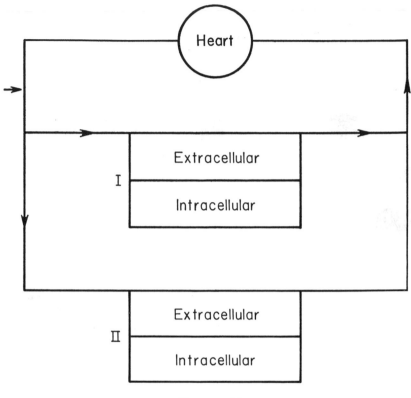

FIGURE 30

drug and chemical concentrations in the extracellular material and then interactions between the concentrations in the extracellular and intracellular regions. These interactions are described by standard chemophysical relations and introduce nonlinearities in an essential way.

The problem is to ascertain the time histories of the concentrations of various agents in organs I and II. We can think of I as the site of interest, and II as an area where side effects are to be minimized. Naturally, the body has more than two organs, but this method will indicate the overall approach.

It may be important to think of joint application of both chemotherapy and radiotherapy with one treatment used to prepare the organ for a more effective use of the other. This method is connected with the control process discussed later.

16. Mathematical Aspects: Differential-difference Equations

Let me indicate some of the return to the mathematician involved in endeavors of this nature. In the usual mathematical models of science and engineering, we encounter vector differential equations of the form

$$\frac{dx}{dt} = g(x), \; x(0) = c. \tag{1}$$

As pointed out repeatedly, and perhaps overly, we possess quite effective techniques for the numerical solution of equations of this type provided that the dimension of x does not exceed several thousand. The situation, however, is much different when we turn to the mathematical description of a physiological process like that described in Sec. 15. The circulation of blood causes part of the output of one organ to return as the input to this organ a certain time later, the time required for the circulation of the blood. The result is that in place of the familiar, reasonably domesticated, equations appearing in Eq. 1, we are led to equations of the form

$$\frac{dx}{dt} = g[x(t), x(t-1)], \; t \geq 1,$$

$$x(t) = h(t), \qquad 0 \leq t \leq 1. \tag{2}$$

These are called *differential-difference equations*. Circulatory phenomena lead naturally to the consideration of time lags.

All types of new analytic and computational questions arise in the consideration of these equations. Many of these questions are decidedly nontrivial. Nonetheless, these equations, in turn, are simplified versions of more complex equations where several time lags enter,

$$\frac{dx}{dt} = g[x(t), x(t-\tau_1), \ldots, x(t-\tau_k)], \tag{3}$$

which are themselves simplified versions of equations of the form

$$\frac{dx}{dt} = g\left[x(t), \int_0^T x(t-s)r(s)ds \right]. \tag{4}$$

In each case, an examination of the physiological validity of the mathematical model leads to a more realistic description involving a still more complex analytic structure. And we have just begun!

17. Computational Solution

Let us now discuss some of the computational aspects of the differential-difference equation of Eq. 16.2. The overwhelming advantage of the conventional differential equation is that we need only store the state at time t_1 in order to determine the subsequent behavior of the system for $t \geqq t_1$. This is a basic property of these equations as far as ease of numerical solution is concerned and, as a matter of fact, is the most important property. We need store only the present state[4] and add the rule for calculating the next state in order to obtain the solution. As soon as this next state has been determined, we can print out the old state and thereby reduce the storage demands on the digital computer.

We can follow the same approach to obtain the numerical solution of a differential-difference equation with the difference that the "state" is now determined by the values of $x(t)$ over the interval of length one, say $[k, k + 1]$. As we upgrade our information at the right-hand end of this interval, $k + 1$, we can eliminate, as before, information at the left-hand end, k. But the problem remains of storing the values of a function over an interval. If $x(t)$ is a high-dimensional vector, say of dimension fifty, and we wish to store $x(t)$ in a unit interval by means of the values at a grid of one thousand points in this interval, we see that we are imposing a demand for a storage capacity of fifty thousand. Even if this demand can be met, we must face the fact that often the solution of systems of the foregoing type represents only a part of the task of analysis of a complex physiological process. Consequently, we cannot go about blithely making demands for a rapid-access storage capacity of fifty thousand or one hundred thousand here and there. This would seriously limit the ability to treat realistic physiological systems.[5]

At first sight, the problem seems insuperable. The equation appears to demand a generalized state vector consisting of the values of a function over an interval of length one. It turns out, however, that we can turn the corner by trading time, which we possess, for

---

[4] In practice, we store the states at some adjacent times in order to calculate the subsequent behavior with enormously increased accuracy.

[5] Another difficulty is that these calculations are often so delicate that they require double and even triple precision, which means doubling or tripling the demands on rapid-access storage.

space, which we do not. We cannot, of course, carry out this trade-off carelessly, because computer time is expensive.

As a matter of fact, this activity is part of a new mathematical game that the computer has introduced. The game is to overcome the limitations of the digital computer, such as a constraint on rapid-access storage, by exploiting its capabilities, notably the solution of large systems of ordinary differential equations, or, in general, the ability to perform iterative algorithms well.

Let me briefly indicate one way of doing this in the foregoing case. In addition to being significant in the study of differential-difference equations, it leads to an unexpected dividend in the application of quasilinearization methods to the solution of large systems of two-point boundary-value problems and, as an application of this ability, to the identification of large systems.

Introduce the sequence of functions

$$x(t + n) = x_n(t), 0 \leq t \leq 1, \tag{1}$$

where $n = 0, 1, 2, \ldots$. Then $x_0(t) = h(t)$ is known. The differential-difference equation assumes the form of an infinite system,

$$\frac{dx_n}{dt} = g(x_n, x_{n-1}), n = 1, 2, \ldots, \tag{2}$$

and we seem to have achieved our objective. The difficulty, however, is that the initial conditions, $x_n(0)$, for $n \geq 2$, are not known. We do, however, know $x_1(0) = h(1)$.

To get around this difficulty, we proceed in the following heavy-handed fashion. Using Eq. 2 we have

$$\frac{dx_1}{dt} = g(x_1, x_0), x_1(0) = c_1 \tag{3}$$

(where $c_1 = h(1)$), which we can use to calculate $x_1(t)$ for $0 \leq t \leq 1$. We suppose at this point that $h(t)$ is a simple function such as a constant, or polynomial in t, which requires no great amount of storage. To continue, we throw away all information concerning $x_1(t)$ except the value $x_1(1) = x_2(0) = c_2$ and consider the two equations

$$\frac{dx_1}{dt} = g(x_1, x_0), x_1(0) = c_1,$$
$$\frac{dx_2}{dt} = g(x_2, x_1), x_2(0) = c_2. \tag{4}$$

From this, we can determine $x_2(1) = x_3(0) = c_3$, which we use to calculate the solution of the system

$$\frac{dx_1}{dt} = g(x_1, x_0),\ x_1(0) = c_1,$$

$$\frac{dx_2}{dt} = g(x_2, x_1),\ x_2(0) = c_2, \tag{5}$$

$$\frac{dx_3}{dt} = g(x_3, x_2),\ x_3(0) = c_3,$$

and so on.[6]

Thus, by solving successively larger systems of ordinary differential equations, we can determine $x(t)$ over any fixed interval $[1, M]$. One advantage of employing ordinary differential equations is that we can use standard computer programs and thus avoid worries of numerical instability associated with new programs specifically written for new types of functional equations.

There is still a major problem associated with carrying out the integration for very large values of M. This problem is basic in all parts of applied mathematics and is a continuing source of difficult questions in mathematical analysis. There are a number of approaches that can be used with some degree of success, notably use of asymptotic behavior, but any discussion of them would lead us too far astray. In any case, no definitive results exist in this area, which requires much additional research.

18. Successive Approximations

An unexpected bonus is provided by the foregoing technique for circumventing storage. It enables us to use the method of successive approximations without imposing excessive demands on the storage capacity of the computer.

Consider, for example, the scalar two-point boundary-value problem

$$u'' = g(u', u),\ u(0) = c,\ u(T) = c_2. \tag{1}$$

If we employ quasilinearization, we obtain a sequence of equations

---

[6] This is analogous to a familiar method for avoiding irrational quantities in algebra. We merely adjoin more equations of rational form. Thus, $i = \sqrt{-1}$ is defined as a solution of $x^2 + 1 = 0$.

$$u''_n = g(u'_{n-1}, u_{n-1}) + (u'_n - u'_{n-1})g_{u'} + (u_n - u_{n-1})g_u,$$
$$u_n(0) = c_1, \ u_n(T) = c_2, \tag{2}$$

where $g_{u'}$ and g_u are evaluated at $u = u_{n-1}$, $u' = u'_{n-1}$. Since the equations are linear, the two-point condition causes no great computational difficulty.[7]

Insofar as actual computation is concerned, obstacles do arise because of the necessity to store the function u_{n-1} over $[0, T]$ while solving for u_n. This is of no particular moment in the scalar case, but for the reasons mentioned, it assumes major significance when vector systems of high dimension are considered.

Fortunately, it turns out that the procedure outlined in Sec. 17 can be readily modified to avoid the necessity for the storage of any functions. At the nth iteration we solve essentially n systems simultaneously. Because the technique of successive approximations obtained from quasilinearization converges quadratically, one seldom encounters equations where more than five iterations are required. Consequently, even for high-dimensional systems there is usually no strain of computer resources. When there is, we can employ the technique described in Sec. 20.

19. Storage and Retrieval of Data

Observe that all the foregoing discussion has been within the domain of the storage and retrieval of data. We have noted that, by making the process as sequential as possible (the introduction of differential equations), we have eliminated a number of problems associated with the storage of data. The same situation exists in the field of pattern recognition where sequential processes, and thus dynamic programming, are assuming a greater and greater role.[8]

How does the brain perform these processes? How much is stored, and how much is recreated when the need arises? How does memory operate, how many memories are there, and what kinds of

---

[7] Nonetheless, it merits close scrutiny inasmuch as it brings in the ability to solve linear systems of algebraic equations, always a matter of some delicacy. Invariant imbedding can be employed to avoid linear systems.

[8] In particular, stochastic approximation, a basic technique originated by Monro and Robbins, has become a major method. It may be viewed as a type of approximation in policy space that can be used to overcome dimensionality difficulties.

memories are they? These questions will not be easily answered, but they are certainly stimulating to the mathematician.

Does the road to a firm grasp on neurophysiology proceed through the study of computers, or conversely? Ten years ago and more, when anthropomorphism was the fad in computers, many people felt that the first attitude was correct. Nowadays, with increasing sophistication and awareness of the subtlety of the problems associated with large systems, the second attitude is prevalent. I subscribe to the belief that we learn new mathematics from what exists, that it does not materialize out of the void. In any case, the days of extravagant claims are over, and serious mathematics has replaced the Sunday supplement feature.

20. Differential Approximation

A more detailed analysis of the chemotherapy process leads to equations with several different time lags, and to equations containing terms of convolution type. These more complex equations pose novel computational problems. To illustrate the point, consider an equation of this nature of very simple structure,

$$\frac{du}{dt} = au + \int_0^t k(t - t_1)u(t_1)dt_1, \, u(0) = c. \tag{1}$$

We can approach this equation along conventional lines by computing the values of $u(t)$ at a set of grid points $(r\Delta)$, $r = 0, 1, \ldots$. One difficulty associated with this straightforward approach is that all the previous values, $[u(r\Delta)]$, $r = 0, 1, \ldots, N$, must be stored to determine the new value $u[N + 1)\Delta]$. As N increases, the storage requirements increase. Again, there is no particular difficulty associated with this in the one-dimensional case, unless we want $u(t)$ for large t, but the multidimensional version can introduce the customary overstrain on rapid-access storage.[9]

To avoid this overstrain, we can proceed in the following way. If

$$k(t) = \sum_{i=1}^{M} b_i e^{\lambda_i t}, \tag{2}$$

---

[9] In the linear case, and certain carefully selected nonlinear cases as well, we can employ Laplace transform techniques.

Eq. 1 becomes

$$\frac{du}{dt} = au + \sum_{i=1}^{M} b_i e^{\lambda_i t} \int_0^t e^{-\lambda_i t_1} u(t_1) dt_1. \tag{3}$$

Write

$$u_i(t) = e^{\lambda_i t} \int_0^t e^{-\lambda_i t_1} u(t_1) dt_1, \; i = 1, 2, \ldots, M. \tag{4}$$

Then

$$\frac{du_i}{dt} = \lambda_i u_i + u, \; u_i(0) = 0, \tag{5}$$

and Eq. 3 becomes

$$\frac{du}{dt} = au + \sum_{i=1}^{M} b_i u_i, \; u(0) = c. \tag{6}$$

Thus, Eq. 5 and 6 constitute a system of ordinary differential equations subject to initial conditions. The numerical solution is direct.

Guided by this fact, we can ask for an approximation to $k(t)$ by an exponential polynomial. Although this type of approximation is notoriously unreliable, there is no need to be dismayed. In place of a direct approximation to $k(t)$, let us seek to determine coefficients $a_1, a_2, \ldots, a_M$ and initial values $c_1, c_2, \ldots, c_M$ so that the solution of the equation

$$v^{(M)} + a_1 v^{(M-1)} + \cdots + u_M v = 0, \; v^{(i)}(0) = c_{i+1}, \tag{7}$$

$i = 0, 1, \ldots, M - 1$, is close to the function $k(t)$. This approach is an example of *differential approximation*.

One way to start the approximation is to determine the a_i which minimize the integral

$$\int_0^T [k^{(M)} + a_1 k^{(M-1)} + \cdots + a_M k]^2 dt, \tag{8}$$

and to use as the values c_i the quantities $k^{(i)}(0)$, $i = 0, 1, \ldots$, $M - 1$. Excellent results can be obtained in this fashion. To obtain more accurate results, we can continue with quasilinearization using a_i and c_i obtained in the foregoing fashion as a first approximation.

The foregoing approach can also be applied to handle nonlinear integral equations of the form

$$u(t) = f(t) + \int_0^T k(|t - t_1|)g(u(t_1))dt_1. \qquad (9)$$

21. Control Theory: Administration of Drugs

Once we have constructed a mathematical model that imitates the behavior of the actual system in sufficient detail, we can begin to study the question of improving the behavior of the system in various ways. In other words, we can begin to attempt the control of the system. In our case, an immediate problem is to determine the kinds of drugs that ought to be administered for various purposes, dosages and ways in which they should be administered, and the combinations of drugs that may prove more efficacious than any individual drug.

With a small amount of additional effort, we can contemplate the construction of an adaptive drug-testing program that will guide us in the choice of a new drug family on the basis of results obtained using the previous drugs.

There are many interesting questions here, most of which require a more detailed understanding of the effect of the concentration of the curative chemical in the organ upon the tumor or cancer.

22. Selfish Aspects of Biomedical Research

I have indicated how new kinds of analytic and computational problems arise readily when we start investigating biomedical systems. Let me now discuss openly the selfish aspects of research of this nature as far as the mathematician is concerned.

As I have pointed out in the two preceding chapters, there is a certain amount of confusion in mathematical circles as to the proper role of the mathematician, what constitutes significant mathematics, and so on. There are even some extremists, ludicrous as it may seem, who esteem those manifestations of the human intellect most removed from human affairs. Consistent with this asceticism, they want mathematics resolutely to be divorced from all interaction with the real world.[10] They think there need be no motivation, and indeed no evidence of the fact that this process is carried out by

[10] This is often called the "St. Simon the Stylite Syndrome."

human beings. Mathematics is to these individuals solely a logical game that could as well be played by computers.

Others—and I am one—feel that interrelations between mathematics and science are absolutely essential; that without the constant spur of scientific necessity, mathematics becomes baroque, sterile, and, even worse, boring. And when a game becomes boring, it has lost its primary function.

I do not believe that there is any way of *proving* which stance is correct, using any generally accepted esthestic axiom system. But if one examines the history of mathematics, there seems to be little question about the relative merits of the two philosophies. The great majority of significant mathematical theories owe their origin to science, and even the classical well-established areas require the infusion of new scientific problems to remain vital.[11] Some mathematicians today claim that times have changed. They feel that there are enough of the Bourbaki ilk, and enough mathematics within this domain, to set up a self-sustaining system. Time will tell, and we can argue the matter again ten years from now. Meanwhile, I insist that I do not believe in self-contained systems that can retain a sense of vitality and intensity.

If you do believe that a vital field of science is a rich source of important mathematical problems, then the field of the biosciences is the proper domain for you. Furthermore, it is the last frontier. The field of physics will never be completely worked out, but the returns these days seem to be marginal compared to the money and manpower expended. However, the field of biology is so rich and complex that one cannot visualize its being exhausted any time in the next hundred or two hundred years. And that is about as far into the future as I feel like either speculating about or worrying about.

If one adds to classical biology the phenomenon of consciousness and contemplates the many new kinds of questions raised by the theories of artificial intelligence, the foregoing statement is certainly reinforced. What is interesting is that the fields of psychosomatic, or somatopsychic, medicine force one to consider both the voluntary and involuntary aspects of the human machine.

Thus the conclusion we reach is that from the practical point of

---

[11] Recall my earlier comments concerning differential equations and the calculus of variations.

view, research in the biomedical domain is the activity for the young mathematician. He will be delving in areas replete with hundreds of new and fascinating problems of both interest and importance where almost no mathematicians have ever set foot before. This is the way both to do good mathematics and to make a name for oneself. Wait until the field becomes fashionable, until the acknowledged intellectual leaders among universities begin spewing forth hundreds of doctorates in these areas, and it will be too late. Respectability is for the middle-aged mathematician.

The young student and the young researcher must understand that the academic world is riddled with fashion. Control theory, for example, is now very, very respectable. It is also correspondingly quite overpopulated.

Thousands of talented young mathematicians strive to perfect an existence and uniqueness theorem in an area where theories were for the asking ten years ago. It is sad to see brilliant young people scrambling after crumbs when banquet tables are waiting in the mathematical biosciences.

Some readers may feel that it is not becoming to talk about practicality, particularly to the very young. One might answer that it is the very young who need the truth most.[12] Furthermore, they can do the most with it. In any case, I feel strongly that idealism and selfishness should be combined in some appropriate mix. It is very well to talk about the idealistic aspects of research in the biomedical fields. But if you want human beings to do it, it is not a bad idea to point out that there are certain practical advantages, too. On the other hand, merely to accentuate the practical would destroy motivation in the young student who desperately needs idealism. However, this is one of the times in history when all the indications are in the same direction.

23. Prosthetics and Orthotics

We can motivate a study of prosthetics and orthotics in two ways, either by an appeal to pragmatism or by an appeal to the imagination. Let us play on the practical theme for a moment.

Prosthetics is the field engaged in replacing lost organs by new ones: artificial arms, legs, hearts, and so on. Orthotics is the field

---

[12] At very least, they need people who are willing to give their opinions as to what the "truth" is.

devoted to improving the performance of an organ that is present but not functioning very well. Orthotics is probably more important at the present time, if only because of the incidence of strokes. As the population that survives becomes older because of the elimination of bacterial and virial enemies, the incidence of stroke victims will increase accordingly. Not a pleasant prospect, but unfortunately the truth.

At the present time, estimates are that about three million people are disabled by strokes. The reliability of the figure is not known, because there is a possibility that many strokes are never diagnosed. The engineering problem is to restore a person to reasonably normal behavior by means of electromechanical devices after some part of his body has been paralyzed due to brain damage. The same problems arise for paraplegics resulting from military action or automobile disasters. It is a question of repairing circuits or redesigning. Can we take a partially disabled person, dependent upon public charity, and restore him to active participation in life?

This problem is very challenging. The idealistic challenge to any human being to use his skills to help another human being to live with dignity cannot be avoided. But let us view here only the scientific aspects. This is a problem in bioengineering, clearly in the field of control theory, and well within the province of computers. The problem forces us to face the bugaboo of "information" once again.

How does a human being carry out even simple actions? Take, for example, the process of extending an arm to pick up an object. A great deal of information processing is going on in the hand-eye-brain complex, but we know very little about it. When faced with the problem of designing a system that will take a hand from here to there, an expert in engineering optimization, experienced in trajectory analysis, may say, "This is a familiar problem. It involves the optimization of a trajectory in six-dimensional phase space. Give me a large enough computer and I can control an artificial arm for you."

This, of course, is the catch. We can't expect a person to trundle a computer around after him. He may possibly expect to use a remote control system feeding into a central computer. Nevertheless, the problem of design of artificial hands and arms along completely classical lines is still much too formidable.

It is hard to believe that the human brain can process data

corresponding to that required to plot the path of a point in six-dimensional phase space.[13] This does not mean that we understand the nature of the actual processing operation. It merely means that if one reviews what is known about the evolutionary development of the brain, it is not credible that it evolved along conventional mathematical lines. What data, then, does the hand-eye-brain use in the casual gesture of reaching out and picking up a piece of chalk?

Can we perhaps get by with estimating only a distance between the hand and the goal and a rate of change of some angle? If so, we have reduced the problem from six dimensions to two dimensions. The data processing can now be carried out quickly and cheaply enough to make feasible the construction of an artificial hand.

It is plausible that the brain uses reduction techniques of this type, combined with an adroit use of feedback control, to perform a number of complex daily tasks. In many cases, it is not clear whether we are depending on conscious effort or using a remembered technique for part of the process. In any case, at present we have no idea how these actions are learned. We can watch children and make some hypotheses about the kinds of learning processes that go on in connection with physical actions, but we are far from any claim to understanding. Thus, we see that these abstract problems concerning reduction of dimensionality, storage of data, and learning processes are very practical problems for the fields of prosthetics and orthotics.

Another interesting point is that there is an intimate connection between these bioengineering problems and those in the mainstream of modern engineering. Probably the basic problem complex in modern society centers about the control of large systems. Our society consists of a number of interacting large complex systems of different types—economic systems, military systems, educational systems, medical systems, and communication systems, to name a few. The major obstacle to the effective operation of large systems is not too little data, but too much data, far too much data and not enough time to process it and abstract the essential information for decisionmaking.

On the other hand, as human beings we are constantly operating

[13] When one begins to investigate operations requiring some manual dexterity, the dimensionality increases alarmingly. There is no harm, however, in trying to solve some simple problems first.

a system far more complex than any man-made system. We do it with apparently little conscious calculations and with very small amounts of input data. How do we do it? This puzzle intrigues the mathematician. Any superficial examination of the problem on classical mathematical grounds would convince us that the activities are impossible. Yet we are living existence proofs that they are possible.

The solution to these puzzles would seem to require new mathematical theories and, indeed, new kinds of mathematical theories.

24. On the Teaching of Doctors

As a final indication of the possible applications of mathematics and computers, let me suggest the problem of contributing to an improved training of doctors. Suppose that we want to aid in teaching medical diagnosis or in instructing psychiatrists in the art of conducting the initial interview of a patient.

Current teaching techniques involve having the student read case histories extensively, observe professionals carrying out the required activities, and finally actually practice as an intern or young resident.

These valuable methods can never be supplanted, but clearly they possess certain drawbacks. Reading case histories is a static process as opposed to the dynamic process involved in actual medical practice. Watching an expert perform a delicate task is much different from being forced simultaneously to do the decisionmaking and carry out the actions oneself. Note we are back to "on-line" control processes! Dealing with live patients as a young physician militates toward conservatism and against being able to practice any new ideas.

Consequently, it would be desirable to have an additional method for teaching by doing that would not involve real people, yet would possess the on-line decisionmaking requirement of actual practice. This problem is the same kind faced by the army in training officers and by business organizations in training executives. Because many of the major decisions are of nonquantitative type, it is not possible to reduce the problem of choosing the appropriate decision to that of solving an equation, determining a maximum value, or following a training manual. The method used to train people in qualitative decisionmaking is *simulation,* one of the important methods of modern systems analysis.

We construct a replica of the actual process and have the individual try his skills in mock situations. If the original process is complex, formidable difficulties occur in imitating the storage, retrieval, and processing of the data involved in simulating a large-scale business or an amphibious invasion. Here is where the computer enters. With the aid of a computer, we can carry out the equivalent of a number of the activities in electronic time as opposed to real time, running through months and years of decisionmaking during only a few hours or days. Using a computer and simulation we can thus experiment with many different organizational techniques and policies.

For example, let me briefly indicate how we could apply this method to teach psychiatric interviewing. We construct a model of a patient with specific symptoms and personality and store all the data in the computer. At the beginning of the interview the trainee, the young psychologist or psychiatrist who is trying to polish his interviewing technique, is given a set of possible questions to ask. Some of these questions are designed to facilitate communication between the psychiatrist and the patient; others are known from experience to impede communication. Each question has a set of associated answers stored in the computer. The answers can be chosen according to a prescribed rule, or we can have an answer chosen according to a certain probability, which depends on the patient's personality and symptoms. Each answer that is given contains a set of associated questions, which is displayed to the trainee. The process continues either for a prescribed time or until certain results are obtained.

If the process has been carefully constructed, the effects of good and bad interviewing techniques can readily be ascertained. It is not difficult to present the basic ideas of simulating an interviewing process, or a diagnostic process, but carrying out the details of the construction requires effort. For example, it is no trivial matter to keep track of all the possible chains of questions and answers to make sure that no contradictions arise, or that the trainee is not asking questions based on information he does not possess. Furthermore, the number of possible chains of dialogue increases at an alarming rate as the number of questions that are allowed increases.

Once simulation processes of this nature have been constructed, we have a systematic means to enable the student to teach himself. He can retire to a computer booth and experiment with various kinds of questioning techniques, or diagnostic methods, without having responsibility for a real patient and without his supervisor peering over his shoulder and asking the reasons for his heretical approaches. All this is intimately tied up with the general subject of teaching machines.

25. Conclusion

I have discussed merely a few of the many new areas of research that have opened up in the biosciences. I have not mentioned vast and exciting areas in genetics, ecology, physiology, neurophysiology, and in the application of stochastic processes.

I did want to emphasize the fact that many opportunities exist for fascinating research at all levels of mathematical ability. For the traditional mathematician, there are new kinds of functional equations and new kinds of control processes to analyze; for the systems analyst, there are novel kinds of systems to explore; for the computer specialist, there are challenges up and down the line to compete with nature and to improve on the results of evolution as far as the storage and retrieval of data are concerned.

One of the most important aspects of the development of these new areas is that it presages a renaissance in human affairs. What has been so bad about much of science is its lack of commitment to the human condition. Human beings, even mathematicians and scientists, need idealism in their daily life. The artificial separation of science and society has had the unfortunate effect of depriving the majority of mathematicians and scientists of a feeling of being committed to something worthwhile, something that counts as far as people are concerned.

As a result, at all levels of the university—faculty, graduate students, and undergraduates—there is the feeling, "Why do it?" It is vital that an intellectual know that the problems he is working on are intrinsically important. It is equally vital to him as a human being to know that his work is relevant to the pressing problems of his society, that the results of his efforts contribute to further the happiness and to alleviate the suffering of other human beings.

Research in the area of cancer, stroke, heart disease, respiratory control, and medical diagnosis brings the intellectual back into contact with his fellows. It allows him to feel involved.

This involvement has been seriously lacking over the last twenty years and has been responsible for much discontent on college campuses. The rise of the mathematical biosciences will change much of this situation by providing the intellectual with the proper combination of challenge and service.

References and Comments

§1. For a discussion of the historical role of the mathematician in science, see:

> Bochner, S. 1966. *The Role of Mathematics in the Rise of Science.* Princeton University Press, Princeton, New Jersey.

A number of scientific journals are devoted wholly or in part to the application of mathematics to biology and medicine:

> *Bulletin of Mathematical Biophysics,* University of Michigan.
> *Computers in Biomedical Research,* Academic Press, Inc.
> *Journal of Theoretical Biology,* Academic Press, Inc.
> *Mathematical Biosciences,* American Elsevier Publishing Company.

Some recent books that treat in detail some of the areas mentioned above are:

> Grodins, F. 1963. *Control Theory and Biological Systems.* Columbia University Press, New York.
> Gurland, J., ed. 1964. *Stochastic Models in Medicine and Biology.* University of Wisconsin Press, Madison.
> Moran, P. A. P. 1962. *The Statistical Processes of Evolutionary Theory.* Clarendon Press, Oxford.
> Rescigno, A., and G. Segre. 1966. *Drug and Tracer Kinetics.* Blaisdell Publishing Company, Waltham, Massachusetts.
> Riggs, D. S. 1963. *The Mathematical Approach to Physiological Problems.* The Williams & Wilkins Company, Baltimore.
> Stibitz, G. R. 1966. *Mathematics in Medicine and the Life Sciences.* Yearbook Medical Publishers, Chicago.

§2. For an expository account of what computers can do in the modern hospital, see:

> Paxton, H. T. 1966. The computer: A report on how it is affecting the hospital physician. *Hospital Physician,* Sept., pp. 35–51.

§3–4. Programs in these areas are being actively pursued at the Los Angeles County General Hospital by Dr. Robert Maronde and Fleur Mitchell.

§6. As examples of the kinds of mathematical problems that arise, see:

> Saksena, J. P. 1967. *Mathematical Model of Scheduling Clients Through*

Welfare Agencies. University of Southern California, USCEE–211. Los Angeles, California.

§7. For an interesting discussion of the difficulties involved in medical diagnosis and the learning process, see the book:

Doctor X. 1965. *Intern.* Harper and Row, New York.

§10. A great deal of work has been done recently in the optical processing of patterns. In particular, some new methods have been developed by J. M. Richardson and associates at the Hughes Research Laboratories in Malibu, California.

§11. For some more detailed discussions, see:

Bellman, R. 1967. Mathematical models of the mind. *Math. Biosci.,* 1: 287–304.

———. 1968. Adaptive processes and intelligent machines. *Proc. Fifth Berkeley Symposium.* Berkeley, California.

Bellman, R., R. Kalaba, and L. Zadeh. 1966. Abstraction and pattern classification. *J. Math. Anal. and Appl.,* 13: 1–7.

In general, articles in the popular press and magazines are either misleading or erroneous.

§12. See:

Bellman, R., and others. 1964. Estimation of heart parameters using skin potential measurements. *Comm. ACM,* 7: 666–68.

———. 1966. Simulated myocardial infarction with a mathematical model of the heart containing distance and boundary effects. *Proc. Long Island Jewish Hospital Symposium on Vectorcardiology.* North Holland Publishing Company, pp. 403–10.

§13. For detailed discussion of the identification of systems, see:

Bellman, R., and R. Kalaba. 1965. *Quasilinearization and Nonlinear Boundary Value Problems.* American Elsevier Publishing Company, New York.

§15. See:

Bellman, R., J. Jacquez, and R. Kalaba. 1960. Some mathematical aspects of chemotherapy—I: One-organ models. *Bull. Math. Biophys.,* 22: 181–98.

———. 1960. Some mathematical aspects of chemotherapy—II: The distribution of a drug in the body. *Bull. Math. Biophys.,* 22: 309–22.

———. 1961. Mathematical models of chemotherapy. *Proc. Fourth Berkeley Symposium on Mathematical Statistics and Probability,* Vol. IV. University of California Press, Berkeley. Pp. 57–66.

§16. See:

Bellman, R., and K. L. Cooke. 1963. *Differential-difference Equations.* Academic Press, Inc., New York.

———. 1965. On the computational solution of a class of functional differential equations. *J. Math. Anal. and Appl.,* 12: 495–500.

Bellman, R., J. Buell, and R. Kalaba. 1965. Numerical integration of a differential-difference equation with a decreasing time lag. *Comm. ACM,* 8: 227–28.

———. 1966. Mathematical experimentation in time-lag modulation. *Comm. ACM,* 9: 752.

Grodins, F. S., J. Buell, and A. J. Bart. 1967. Mathematical analysis and digital simulation of the respiratory control system. *J. Appl. Physiol.,* 22: 260–76.

§17–18. See:

Bellman, R. 1961. Successive approximations and computer storage problems in ordinary differential equations. *Comm. ACM,* 4: 222–23.

———. 1962. From chemotherapy to computers to trajectories. *Mathematical Problems in the Biological Sciences.* Proceedings of the Fourteenth Symposium in Applied Mathematics of the American Mathematical Society. American Mathematical Society, Providence, Rhode Island.

§20. See:

Bellman, R., and R. Kalaba. 1965. *Quasilinearization and Nonlinear Boundary Value Problems.* American Elsevier Publishing Company, Inc., New York.

Bellman, R., R. Kalaba, and J. Lockett. 1966. *Numerical Inversion of the Laplace Transform.* American Elsevier Publishing Company, New York.

§23. See:

Bellman, R. 1965. Mathematical aspects of the theory of systems. *Proceedings.* Jerome Fox, ed. Symposium on System Theory. Polytechnic Institute of Brooklyn, Microwave Research Institute, Symposia series, Vol. 15. Polytechnic Press of the Polytechnic Institute of Brooklyn, New York.

———. 1968. On the construction of a mathematical theory of the identification of systems. *Proc. Fifth Berkeley Symposium.* Berkeley, California.

§24. See:

Bellman, R., M. B. Friend, and L. Kurland. 1966. On the construction of a simulation of the initial psychiatric interview. *Behavioral Sci.,* 11: 389–99.

———. 1967. *A Simulation of the Initial Psychiatric Interview.* The RAND Corporation, R-449-RC, Santa Monica, Calif.

Colby, K. M. 1963. Computer simulation of a neurotic process. *Computer Simulation of Personality.* John Wiley & Sons, New York. Pp. 165–79.

———. 1964. Experimental treatment of neurotic computer programs. *Arch. Gen. Psychiatry,* 10: 220–27.

———. 1965. Computer simulation of neurotic processes. *Computers in Biomedical Research,* 1: 491–503.

————. 1967. Computer simulation of change in personal belief systems. *Behavioral Sci.* (in press).

Colby, K. M., and J. P. Gilbert. 1964. Programming a computer model of neurosis. *J. Math. Psychol.*, 1: 405–17.

Colby, K. M., J. Watt, and J. P. Gilbert. 1966. A computer method of psychotherapy. *J. Nerv. Ment. Dis.*, 142: 148–52.

INDEX